The Challenge of

THE SEA

The Challenge of

THE SEA

ARTHUR C. CLARKE

Illustrated by Alex Schomburg
Introduction by Wernher von Braun

HOLT, RINEHART AND WINSTON

NEW YORK CHICAGO SAN FRANCISCO

Copyright © 1960 BY ARTHUR C. CLARKE

ACKNOWLEDGMENTS

Many people have helped me to collect material for this book, but I would not like to saddle them with the opinions and ideas put forward in it.

My particular thanks are due to Dr. William K. Emerson, Dr. Vladimir Walters and John Purcell, at the American Museum of Natural History; Dr. Carleton Ray and Dr. Ross F. Nigrelli at the New York Aquarium; Dr. F. G. Wood, curator of the Marineland Research Laboratory, Saint Augustine, Florida; and John L. Mero, Institute of Marine Resources, University of California.

I am also grateful to the Curtis Publishing Company for permission to reprint sections of chapter twelve, which originally appeared in *Holiday* magazine.

Library of Congress Catalog Card Number 60-11244

91464–0412

contents

BY THE SAME AUTHOR

Fiction

ISLANDS IN THE SKY
PRELUDE TO SPACE
AGAINST THE FALL OF NIGHT
THE SANDS OF MARS
CHILDHOOD'S END
EXPEDITION TO EARTH
EARTHLIGHT
REACH FOR TOMORROW
THE CITY AND THE STARS
TALES FROM THE 'WHITE HART'
THE DEEP RANGE
THE OTHER SIDE OF THE SKY
ACROSS THE SEA OF STARS

Nonfiction

INTERPLANETARY FLIGHT
THE EXPLORATION OF SPACE
GOING INTO SPACE
THE COAST OF CORAL
THE MAKING OF A MOON
THE REEFS OF TAPROBANE
VOICE ACROSS THE SEA
THE CHALLENGE OF THE SPACESHIP

With Mike Wilson

THE FIRST FIVE FATHOMS
BOY BENEATH THE SEA

With R. A. Smith

THE EXPLORATION OF THE MOON

You may think it strange that I, of all people, should be writing an introduction to a book on the challenge of the sea. But, in a way, I owe it to my friend Arthur Clarke. For it was he who introduced me to the sport that has rapidly become my favorite— skin diving. On the other hand, you may wonder that Arthur Clarke, the author of *Interplanetary Flight, The Exploration of Space,* and *Going into Space,* would write a book about the sea. However, there is a close relationship between the sea and space. From a poetical, but not too farfetched, viewpoint, we on earth can consider the bottom of our sea as man's point of departure on his extremely long trip to outer space. Life began in the depths of the sea, and through eons moved upward to the land. Today, after a brief pause, he has the means for continuing his journey from the land upward through the atmospheric sea to the reaches beyond the sun and its satellites, both natural and artificial.

The sea around us, to borrow the title of Miss Rachel Carson's wonderful book, has always worked a strange fascination on the mind of man. Perhaps the sight of it evokes subconscious and vestigial memories of his primal beginning. At any rate, I believe that man's insatiable longing for knowledge of what lies beneath the sea stems from the same source as that which prompts him to wonder whether there is life on Mars. Daily, we are learning more and more about the wonders of the sea and the solar system. But we have merely scratched the surface of both. Whether thinking of the sea or space, I am of the same mind as my friend Arthur Clarke, who writes in this book, "Perhaps as our knowledge grows, the sea will lose some of its mystery and magic—but I do not think so. As far ahead as imagination can roam, there will be unexplored depths, lonely islands, endless leagues of ocean upon which a lost ship could wander for weeks without sighting land. When the continents have been tamed from pole to pole, when all the deserts have been irrigated, the forests cleared, the polar icecap melted—much of the sea will still remain an untouched wilderness."

Wernher von Braun

vii

chapter 1

The World of Water

Imagine that you are walking along the edge of the sea on a bright summer day when the waves come rolling in to break gently at your feet. Right out to the far horizon the miles of blue water stretch beneath the sun. There is not a single ship in sight — nothing moves in all that vast expanse of water, except the waves beating forever against the sand.

How empty, how lifeless the sea looks on such a day. And above all, how peaceful. But it is none of these things. When it is stirred up by storms it can smash the mightiest ships that man has ever built. And as for being empty, it is so full of life that, by contrast, the land is a desert.

For all life — you and I, the eagle and the elephant, the rabbit and the rattlesnake, the hummingbird and the butterfly, any creatures you care to mention — came from the sea. And most of the world's life is still there.

Go down to the water's edge and scoop up a handful of the salty liquid which covers almost three-quarters of the planet we have misnamed Earth. What do you see? Probably nothing but plain, clear water. Yet if you had a microscope, that handful of water would appear as it really is, a jungle in which millions of fantastic creatures battle for existence. No beings from outer space could be more weird than some of the plants and animals that inhabit the oceans of our own world.

The sea holds not only the smallest, but also the largest of all living things. We sometimes look in awe at pictures of the giant dinosaurs that walked the earth millions of years ago. Some of them weighed thirty tons, and the ground must have trembled beneath their footsteps. Yet the blue whale of today is five times as heavy as the greatest dinosaur that ever lived.

There are other giants in the sea — some we have discovered, but others are still unknown. We may never complete the roll call of the sea's creatures. A thousand years from now, when we have explored many strange worlds in space, we may still be finding weird beasts far down in the ocean deeps.

At a time when there is so much concern with travel in and beyond the atmosphere, interest in the sea may seem a little old-fashioned. Nothing could be further from the truth. The sea still carries much the largest part of the world's international trade. It will be a long time before we can send by air the millions upon millions of tons of cargo which pass through our great ports every year. And now that the first nuclear-powered ships are being built, we are about to witness a revolution in transport both above and below the surface of the sea.

There are even better reasons why the sea is becoming steadily more important to us. We are using up the resources of the land at a terrifying rate, exhausting its supplies of coal, oil, minerals — above all, of food. Many of the metals upon which our civilization depends have almost gone. You may live to see copper become as rare and valuable as silver.

Yet in and under the ocean there are enough raw materials to supply all our needs for a million years. Can we get at them? Well, we have already started. It may surprise you to learn that men have been "mining the ocean" for almost twenty years, and that much of the metal in a modern airplane comes from sea water! But we must do far better if we hope to save our machine-based civilization from collapsing back into the Stone Age through shortage of metals.

It is in the sea that we may have to grapple with the greatest of all the problems that confront us — one beside which the hydrogen bomb is merely a mild nuisance. Already, a third of the human race does not get enough to eat. Yet every day, a hundred thousand new mouths come into the world. In the time it takes you to read this book, the family of mankind will have grown enough to populate a small town.

How are we going to feed the new millions of tomorrow? It seems more and more likely that the answer will be found in the sea. For perhaps twenty thousand years, man has farmed the land. Within the next twenty, he must learn to farm the sea. There is little time to lose if we hope to avoid mass starvation before this century draws to its close.

Let us turn to more cheerful subjects. The sea is not only involved in the coming struggle for existence, it is one of the great playgrounds of the future. Perhaps you have already put on flippers and face mask and have swum through the submarine fairyland that, a few years ago, was known only to a handful of deep-sea divers. The invention of skin-diving gear has opened up a whole new world of sport and recreation as well as of scientific research.

It has also led to unexpected discoveries in other directions. Everyone has heard tales of sunken treasure, and some of these stories are true. Much of the wealth of mankind lies at the bottom of the sea in the wrecks of a million ships from Roman galleys to turbine-powered liners. But perhaps the greatest treasures in the sea are not gold or silver, but marble and bronze, for countless lost works of art are lying safely preserved in the mud of centuries. In recent years a few of them have been recovered — but only a very few. It has been said that the floor of the Mediterranean is the greatest museum in the world. It is a museum we have just begun to explore.

And so the sea holds both the past and the future of mankind. This book is about that future.

chapter *2*

The Shape of the Sea

ALTHOUGH men have been sailing the seas for at least five thousand years, it was only during the nineteenth century that they discovered the true size and shape of the oceans. The maps showed that there was much more sea than land — about three-quarters of the earth is covered with water — but how deep that water was no one knew. Only near the shore was it possible to reach bottom with a sounding line — a heavy weight or lead tied to the end of a rope. When they tried this in the open sea, hundreds of miles from the nearest land, the old-time sailors failed to touch the bottom. Their lines were too short, and anyway they weren't particularly interested. As long as the water was deep enough to sail in — that was the only thing that mattered to them. From their point of view it was all the same whether the ocean was one mile or a hundred miles deep. What practical importance was it to anyone to know how far down the sea bed was? Only a few long-haired scientists were interested in such things.

And then, just over a hundred years ago, the depths of the sea suddenly became of very great importance to all civilized countries. The invention of the electric telegraph, early in the nineteenth century, made it possible to send messages thousands of miles in a few seconds between any two points where wires could be laid. Naturally, it was not long before men started to think about laying a cable across the Atlantic, so that Europe and America could talk to each

other with the speed of electricity instead of having to wait
weeks for ships to make the crossing. (The story of the Atlantic cables will be found in my book, *Voice Across the Sea*.)
But before a trans-Atlantic cable could be laid it was necessary to know the depth of the Atlantic, and also the nature
of its bed. And so, in the 1850's the first real deep-sea surveys
were carried out by the British and American navies, along
a line that joined Newfoundland and Ireland.

It took hours to make each measurement, for the ship
had to be stopped, the heavily weighted line lowered to the
bottom, and then the two or three miles of rope hauled up
again. But slowly the picture of the Atlantic sea bed built
up on the charts — the outlines of hills and valleys that no
man had ever seen, the shapes of sunken mountains rising
from great plains of mud that had gathered for a million
years. Because the depth measurements, or soundings, took
so long to make, there were a good many miles between
each one, and so the map of the sea bed was very far from
being complete. In fact, it was full of gaps, yet it was still
a great achievement. The scientists and naval officers who
carried out these early surveys were rather like men floating
high across the United States in a balloon, trying — in complete darkness — to discover the shape of the land beneath
them by letting down a weight on a piece of string. Such a
slow and crude method of measurement would give fairly
good results over the flat states of the Midwest, but it could
give only a very rough picture of the Rockies. It might even
miss completely something as large as the Grand Canyon.

We should not be surprised, therefore, that the first surveys of the North Atlantic showed the sea bed to be much
smoother and flatter than it really is. Perhaps this was a
good thing. If the scientists of the 1850's had known all its
ups and downs, they would have been so discouraged that

they might not have tried to lay a cable across it. According to their measurements, most of the North Atlantic sea bed was a fairly level plain (christened Telegraph Plateau) about two miles down, and at no point was the ocean more than two and a half miles deep.

As we shall see later, the true picture is much more complicated, and how this was discovered is a fascinating example of the way in which modern science has allowed us to learn things about the deep sea which could never have been guessed when our grandparents were children. The invention that allows us to map the bed of the ocean with such speed and accuracy that we can almost see it is the echo-sounder.

The principle of the echo-sounder is extremely simple, and you can demonstrate it yourself quite easily if you stand about fifty feet away from a high wall or a tall building. (The best place to try the experiment is in a narrow, dead-end street, with walls all around you.) If you clap your hands or stamp your feet you'll hear an echo coming back a fraction of a second later, faint but clear. It is the noise you made returning to you after being reflected from the far wall. There may be several echoes from walls at different distances.

Let's suppose that you hear the main echo just a tenth of a second after you've made the noise. Sound moves through the air at about a thousand feet a second (the speed varies with the temperature, but let's not worry about that at the moment). So your echo must have traveled a hundred feet, and this means that the wall must be fifty feet away — since the sound has to make the round trip there and back.

The idea of using underwater sounds to get echoes from the sea bed, and so to measure its depth, now seems very obvious and elementary, but not until 1920 was it put into practice. The modern echo-sounder employs a kind of loud-

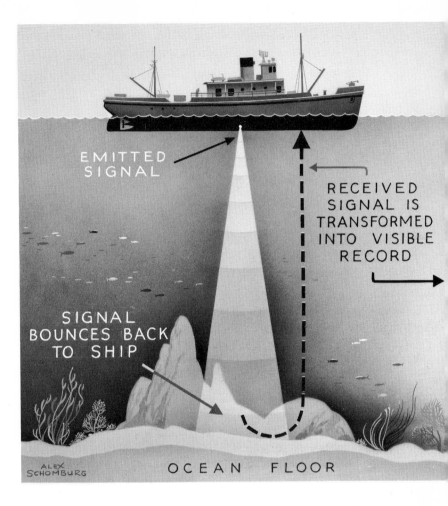

EMITTED SIGNAL

RECEIVED SIGNAL IS TRANSFORMED INTO VISIBLE RECORD

SIGNAL BOUNCES BACK TO SHIP

OCEAN FLOOR

ALEX SCHOMBURG

speaker attached to the hull of the ship below the water line, and every few seconds this shoots a sudden, high-pitched shriek down toward the sea bed. The returning echo is picked up by a microphone, and appears as a spot on a moving chart or on a screen like that of a TV set. And so, as the ship sails along, the echo-sounder can draw a continuous picture of the sea bed below it — a picture so accurate that it will show wrecks and even schools of fish. What a contrast to the old days when a ship had to stay

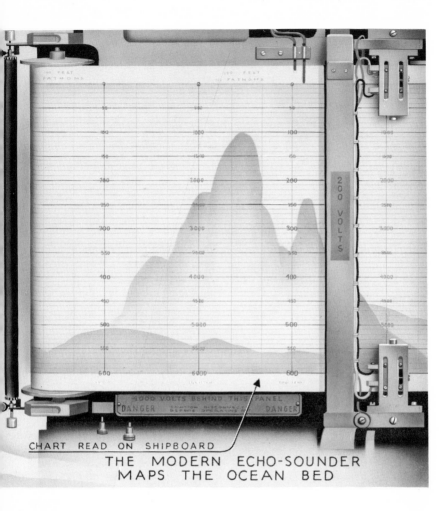

CHART READ ON SHIPBOARD

THE MODERN ECHO-SOUNDER
MAPS THE OCEAN BED

fixed for hours to make a single sounding! Now it takes only seconds, and the ship can travel at full speed.

The echo-sounder is a fine example of the way in which a new invention — often quite a simple one — can revolutionize some branch of science. It happened in astronomy when the first telescope was built, and in biology when the microscope was invented. In fact, almost all our knowledge of the deep sea has been gained by the use of special instruments of some kind or other, and more are being built all the time. But we shall need many, many more before we can understand all the mysteries of the ocean.

Some of those mysteries concern the shape of the sea bed, now revealed to us in detail by the echo-sounder — although there are still enormous areas uncharted, especially in the Pacific. Perhaps the best way to picture the floor of the ocean is to imagine that you are driving out from land in a kind of submarine tank that can crawl along the sea bed. Such vehicles have been built, although none that can go as deep as we shall pretend. We'll also assume that we can see as far underwater as we can on land, so that we can look at the hills and valleys around us. In actual fact, you can seldom see more than a hundred feet underwater, and visibility is usually very much poorer than this. A diver often considers himself lucky when he can see ten feet.

Well, here we go! The water gurgles around the conning tower as we sink beneath the waves. Ahead lies an immense plain of sand and mud, with occasional rocks and boulders scattered across it — not to mention dozens of wrecks in various stages of decay. We are on the edge of the continental shelf, the wide, gently sloping platform that surrounds most of the world's major land masses. You will have to look very closely to see that it is sloping at all. Our submarine tank may have to travel miles out from land before the water reaches a depth of five hundred feet. On the average, the continental shelf is about thirty miles wide, although in places like the Grand Banks of Newfoundland, it stretches for several hundred miles.

But at last the shelf comes to an end. Fairly suddenly, the sea bed starts to angle downward. We have entered the zone known as the slope, and it is like driving down a very gentle hill. Mile after mile we descend while the depth of the water mounts above us. Now we must measure our

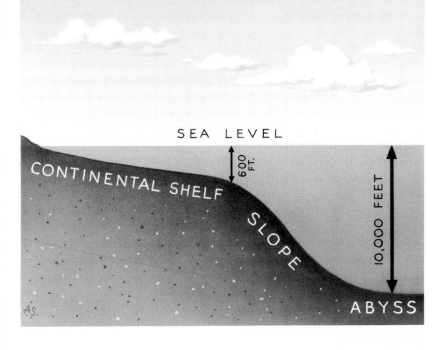

SEA LEVEL

CONTINENTAL SHELF

SLOPE

600 FT.

10,000 FEET

ABYSS

distance to the surface not in hundreds, but in thousands of feet. We passed the five-thousand-foot line long ago. Now we are at ten thousand feet — almost two miles down. The descent, however, is no longer so rapid; the slope is flattening out. Presently we are moving once more across a level plain which stretches for hundreds of miles ahead of us. We have reached the abyss, the true floor of the ocean.

Continental shelf, slope, abyss — these are the three main regions into which the ocean is divided. On the average, the abyss is about two and a half miles down — but this figure is nothing like the greatest depth in the sea, for the journey I have described was a very smooth and uneventful one. It completely missed the strangest and most spectacular features of the sea bed.

If we had started out to sea in some parts of the world —

off the mouth of the Hudson River, for example — we would have found that both the continental shelf and the slope beyond it were torn and gashed by enormous valleys or chasms, some of them a hundred miles long and ten or twenty miles wide. These sunken canyons, greater than any on the dry land, would be awe-inspiring sights if they were visible to the eye; but we know them only through the readings of the echo-sounder. Some of them are mightier than the Grand Canyon, which is perhaps the most impressive spectacle on the surface of the earth.

Now here is a major mystery. The Grand Canyon was formed by the action of the Colorado River slowly carving away the rock, century by century. The river is still doing its work, as anyone can see who has looked down into the canyon and watched the muddy waters moving far below. But these great canyons in the sea — how were *they* formed? Some of them are a mile deep, and it's hard to imagine rivers flowing at the bottom of the sea!

Yet there are rivers in the sea, some of them bigger than the Mississippi. One theory is that great submarine currents carved these gorges leading down to the ocean deeps. Another is that the level of the sea has risen so far — or the land has dropped so much — that these regions of the sea bed were once dry land through which some ancestor of the Colorado River flowed millions of years ago. It is almost impossible to imagine such vast upheavals of land and sea. If they are still going on, it may mean that one day the Grand Canyon will be a mile below water, perplexing the scientists of the far future.

The mysterious canyons belong to the edges of the continents, but further out in the open sea are much deeper gorges. In these trenches, as they are called, are the greatest of all ocean depths. Soundings of over thirty-six thousand feet have been made in the Pacific, off the Marianas. If Mount Everest were sunk in the Marianas Trench, its summit would still be a mile below sea level.

The ocean contains mountains as well as valleys. Some of these mountains have been known since the earliest times, for their peaks rise above the water to form islands such as the Azores. But many more are completely submerged and have been discovered only recently. The greatest mountain range on earth is not on any of the continents, but halfway between America and Europe. For seven thousand miles the Atlantic Ridge runs southward from Iceland almost to the Antarctic Circle, spanning a third of the circumference of the globe. In places it soars two miles above the sea bed — yet even then it misses the surface by a mile.

During the war a scientist, who also happened to be the commanding officer of a United States Navy transport, discovered a new type of undersea mountain recorded on the charts of his echo-sounder. In many parts of the Pacific, isolated flat-topped mountains rise abruptly from the sea bed — sunken mesas as much as a mile below the surface. Samples dredged from the tops of these hidden plateaus show that they are the stumps of mountains that towered above the sea, perhaps a hundred million years ago. The rains and the waves of centuries wore them down to sea-level, thus producing their flat tops. And then, quite suddenly (as time is measured by the geologists) they sank into the depths of the Pacific where they remain to this day as fossil mountains from the Age of Reptiles, holding unknown secrets from the past.

The ocean bed, therefore, contains even more varied scenery than the dry land; its mountain ranges are longer, its canyons wider and deeper than any on the continents. It will be many years before we have mapped it completely

— and many more before we have explored it in detail, for
the sheer volume of the sea is almost beyond human imagination. It does not convey much to say that the oceans
contain 300 million cubic miles of water, but perhaps this
fact will help you to get this enormous figure into perspec-
tive: There is enough water in the sea to provide every
man, woman and child on earth with a private swimming
pool a mile long, a mile wide — and five hundred feet deep.

And, of course, the sea is not merely plain water. It is a
world of life and energy, sometimes calm and peaceful,
sometimes shaken by storms and blasted by submarine
volcanoes. Even down in the abyss, two or three miles
below the waves, the water is not wholly still, but moves
in sluggish currents that ripple the deep-sea muds and oozes.
Deeper yet, in the great trenches six miles from the last
light of the sun, one might expect to find eternal calm. But
this is not so, for the trenches are the birthplace of earthquakes which may send tidal waves spreading death and
destruction for thousands of miles.

Enormous, wonderful and even terrifying, is the strange
world waiting for us beneath the waves. Let us see how
men have entered it in the past — and how they hope to
explore it in the future.

chapter 3

Men Among Fish

THERE is a legend that, twenty-two centuries ago, Alexander the Great descended into the sea in an airtight box to observe the creatures there. This story may well be true, even if we doubt the rest of the tale — that he saw a fish so huge that it took three days to swim past although it was moving as swiftly as a flash of lightning. Since the speed of a lightning stroke is about twenty million miles an hour, this sea monster must have been a billion and a half miles long. Some fish!

Long before the time of Alexander, men had been diving into the sea in search of pearls, precious corals, and sponges. There were even ancestors of our modern frogmen, complete with snorkel breathing tubes, four or five hundred years before Christ. They took part in the naval battles between Athens and Sparta, so we must not think that underwater warfare is a modern invention.

However, these earlier divers could descend only a short distance below the surface, and could not stay submerged for more than a couple of minutes since they had to depend on their own lung power. Swimming underwater while holding your breath is about the most exhausting activity there is, and native pearl-divers seldom live to a ripe old age even if they escape accident. The greatest depth ever reached by a diver without any form of breathing-gear is about two hundred feet, but the normal limit for this kind of diving is only fifty or sixty feet. This is quite far enough for most people if they have to swim back to the surface on the same lungful of air.

The first serious attempts to build machines which would enable men to descend to considerable depths, and to stay there for reasonable lengths of time, began about four hundred years ago. From the sixteenth century onward, all sorts of inventors produced odd-looking diving bells and underwater breathing gadgets, very few of which actually worked. But some did, and were used to salvage valuables from wrecks. One of the earliest — and most successful — of all hunts for sunken treasure took place as long ago as 1687 when William Phips used a diving bell to lift a million and a half dollars in gold from the wreck of a Spanish galleon in the Bahamas. Few later treasure hunters have been so fortunate.

The diving bell is such a simple device that it must have

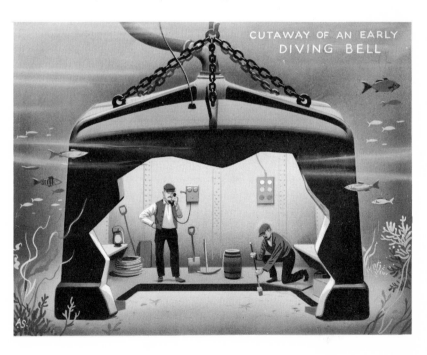

CUTAWAY OF AN EARLY
DIVING BELL

been invented many times and in many places. We shall probably never know the name of the first brave man who tried it out. You can demonstrate its principle very easily by lowering an empty glass, open end downward, into a bucket of water. The glass remains full of air even when it is completely submerged. If you look carefully, however, you will notice that the water has risen a little way into the glass, and the further down you push it, the more the water level will rise inside. But there will always be some air in the top, and you would have to sink the glass more than thirty feet before it would become half full of water.

The first diving bells were merely strong wooden or metal boxes, open at the bottom, and heavily weighted so that they would sink in spite of the air inside them. Men were able to work in them for an hour or more, picking up objects off the sea bed or salvaging cannon from wrecks, before the air became too bad to breathe. By the eighteenth century, pumps had been invented that could force fresh air down from the surface, and anyone who wished to do so could then stay underwater all day if he felt like it. But he couldn't see much, and diving bells were so heavy and clumsy that it was difficult to move them around. Something better was needed. Something that would allow a man to walk about on the sea bed, and would also permit him to go to greater depths.

It arrived in 1819 when August Siebe invented the diving suit which still bears his name and which, more than a hundred years later, has only been improved in minor details. The deep-sea diver with his rubber suit, air hose and heavy copper helmet became a familiar figure in every ocean and every port — although the description, "deep-sea," is rather misleading, for it is rare for men using this type of gear to descend more than a hundred feet, and

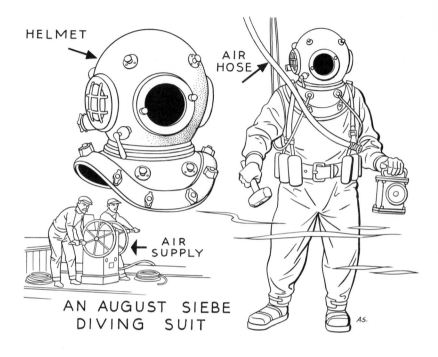

HELMET

AIR HOSE

AIR SUPPLY

AN AUGUST SIEBE
DIVING SUIT

unsafe for them to go down more than about three hundred feet.

After the diving suit, the next great underwater breakthrough was the famous Aqua-lung, invented in 1943 by Captain Cousteau and Emile Gagnan. The tremendous importance of the Aqua-lung was that for the first time men were able to swim around freely underwater without any connection with the surface, for they carried their own self-contained air supply. Moreover, because it is simple and safe to use — provided that it is handled with common sense — the Aqua-lung allows almost anybody to dive. For centuries only the professional divers were able to go into the sea. Today hundreds of thousands of ordinary people are exploring the marvelous world beneath the waves. There is no doubt that much of the present great interest in the sea comes from this fact.

The limit of safe Aqua-lung diving is about three hundred feet, and only experts can go as far down as this. The practical limit is more like two hundred, and even that requires careful training. It seems, therefore, that a kind of depth barrier exists about a hundred yards down, beyond which divers cannot pass without great danger whether they are using self-contained breathing apparatus of the Aqua-lung type, or the earlier diving suit with an air hose to the surface.

A hundred yards isn't much of a distance — men have run that far in less than ten seconds. And it looks very small indeed compared with the almost thirty-six thousand feet of the greatest ocean depth. What is the cause of this depth barrier, and is there any way of breaking through it?

To answer this question we have to consider something that doesn't worry us much in ordinary, everyday life — pressure. Here on the surface of the earth, we land animals are at the bottom of a deep ocean of air. Now, air has weight — a good deal more than you might think. The weight of the air inside a large house may be more than a ton. Every moment of your life, you are supporting the weight of the long column of air above your body, right up to the top of the atmosphere. On every square inch — that's an area about the size of a big postage stamp — the weight of the air pressing down works out at about fifteen pounds. Over your whole body this adds up to the amazing total of between ten and fifteen tons.

The reason why you don't feel this weight, and aren't crushed by it at once, is because there is also air inside your body — in the lungs — pushing outward with the same force. So the two weights are balanced, and you don't even know that they're there. If the balance were not perfect, you would not be able to breathe. The weight on your chest would be so great that you could not expand your lungs.

All this pressure is due to the invisible sea of air above us, but water weighs eight hundred times as much as air and can exert a very much greater pressure. When you dive down thirty-three feet, the weight of water above you equals that of all the miles of air right up to the top of the strato-sphere, and the pressure increases at the same rate all the way to the bottom of the sea. If you go down thirty-three thousand feet — which no one has yet done — the pressure would be a thousand times as great as we experience at sea level, or fifteen thousand pounds on every square inch. These enormous, crushing pressures are the biggest obstacle to really deep dives into the ocean, and we will see later some of the ways in which they may be overcome.

Let's stick to more modest depths at the moment, and consider what happens to a diver three hundred and thirty feet down where the water pressure comes to just ten times that of the air you are breathing at the moment (unless you happen to be on a mountaintop or in an airliner). He will be able to breathe only if air is pumped down to him, or is fed into his lungs from an Aqua-lung, at ten times normal pressure. If the air reaches him at less than this pressure, his chest will collapse owing to the weight of the water. The old-time helmet-divers had a word for this — the squeeze. It killed a good many of them when their pumps failed to deliver enough air.

Now air at ten times normal pressure is getting rather thick. Men can breathe it, but it's really too rich for proper human consumption. In fact, it produces an effect very much like strong drink. After a few minutes in air at several times normal pressure, most people start to behave as if they are intoxicated, and many become unconscious. They re-cover when the pressure is reduced, and there's no hangover or other ill effect. But a diver three hundred feet down can't afford to be drunk, any more than a motorist can. He has only to make one slip, and he's dead.

For many years, scientists have been trying to discover just why compressed air has this strange effect on the human body. Air is a rather complicated gas, consisting of seventy-eight per cent nitrogen, twenty-one per cent oxygen, and one per cent other gases. The oxygen is the important part — without this life-giving gas, we would die in a couple of minutes. Nitrogen, on the other hand, goes in and out of the lungs without doing anything. As far as our bodies are concerned, it might as well not be there.

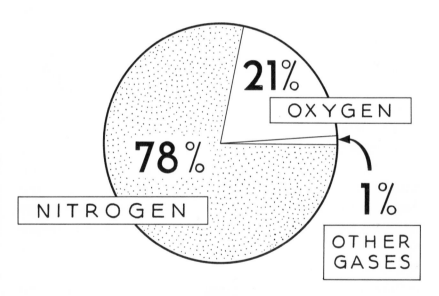

THE COMPONENTS OF AIR

This is no longer true at very high pressures. Nitrogen then becomes mildly intoxicating, and the effect gets worse as the pressure increases. The delightful phrase, "rapture of the depths," has been coined to describe the symptoms, and a lot of effort has gone into finding how to avoid them. The only thing that can be done is to replace the nitrogen in air by some gas that won't have an intoxicating effect, but unfortunately there are not many alternatives. Two that have been tried are hydrogen and helium. The first is dangerous because it is highly explosive, and the second is expensive. Using either involves great technical complications and highly trained men.

In 1945 a courageous young Swede named Arne Zetterstrom descended to 528 feet breathing a mixture of hydrogen and oxygen. Unfortunately, a mistake on the part of the men hauling him up resulted in his death. Three years later, in 1948, a British Royal Navy diver, William Bollard, reached a depth of 540 feet using helium and oxygen. In 1956 the Royal Navy pushed this record down to 600 feet, using the same technique. The fact that it has taken 11 years to go an extra 72 feet proves how difficult it is to make further progress in deep diving.

For even when we have solved the problem of nitrogen intoxication by getting rid of the nitrogen, there is another peril to be faced. Very high pressure forces gas into the bloodstream and the tissues of the body, and when the diver returns to the surface from a great depth, the reduction in pressure allows this dissolved gas to start bubbling out again. The result is the dreaded complaint known as "the bends," because the pain in the joints often makes the unfortunate diver double up in agony. Severe cases of the bends can produce permanent paralysis and even death.

There is only one way to avoid this danger, perhaps the greatest which divers have to face. That is to come back to the surface so slowly that the gas dissolved in the body has time to work its way out harmlessly. But — and this is a very big but — this means that it takes literally hours to bring a deep diver back to normal atmospheric pressure. He has to stop at carefully calculated depths on the way up and wait there until it is safe to go. Alternatively, he has to be sealed up in a kind of overgrown pressure cooker known as a decompression chamber, and left there while the air is slowly let out. When William Bollard made his record descent, he was on the sea bed for only five minutes — but he had to spend eight and a half hours in the decompression chamber while the oxygen and helium worked its way out of his body.

The case for really deep descents by men using diving suits or any form of breathing apparatus, therefore, looks rather hopeless. If we wish to go further down than five hundred feet, it seems that we will always be forced to stay inside the protective walls of submarine vehicles like Professor Piccard's bathyscape. In these vessels men breathe normal air because the strong walls around them take up the pressure of the sea, and so there is no limit to the depth that can be reached — as long, of course, as the metal is strong enough to withstand the tons of water pressing down on every square inch.

Yet scientific diving is less than a hundred years old, and we still have much to learn about the sea and our bodies' reactions to it. Perhaps the dangers and difficulties which seem so great today will be overcome by new inventions and techniques, as has happened so many times in the past. It is always risky to say that something is impossible if it is worth doing (and we'll come back to that later). Men without any protection may one day work for long periods even at depths of a thousand feet, under pressures thirty times as great as those at the earth's surface.

In the assault on Mount Everest, the climbers spent many days living in camps at steadily increasing altitudes so that their bodies had time to adjust to the low pressure. They did not try to reach the top and come back again in a few hours. In the same way, the deep divers of the future will have to stay underwater for weeks or even months at a time. Men have already done this in some of the modern submarines, so the idea of a permanent underwater base is not so fantastic. Let us, therefore, throw our imaginations twenty or fifty years into the future and visit a true undersea research station out on the edge of the continental shelf.

The deep-sea lab is six hundred feet down, at the beginning of the long slope that leads into the abyss more than two miles below. It is a group of metal spheres and stubby cylinders, joined together with connecting tubes, anchored in the bedrock and very strongly built. Although six hundred feet is a mere fraction of the ocean's greatest depth, there is a pressure of twenty tons on every square

AN UNDERSEA
RESEARCH STATION
OF THE FUTURE

foot of the structure. On each section of the lab's walls the water presses inward with the weight of two elephants.

And yet, men are venturing out into that frightful, crushing darkness. A thick circular door opens in the side of the lab, and in the glare of underwater searchlights a strange procession emerges. First comes a streamlined sled, moving slowly out of the air lock under the drive of its concealed propellers. Its pilot is lying prone behind the low windshield that protects him from the slip stream. On his control board are instruments that tell speed, depth, compass heading, fuel reserve. There is even a device that looks like a radio, but as radio waves will not travel more than a few feet through water, it operates on pulses of sound too high-pitched for human ears to detect. By means of this sonar set the explorers can signal to base, and can also locate obstacles in the water around them.

Behind the sled are two smaller machines looking very much like torpedoes. Each has a man riding on it, gripping handle bars exactly like those of a motor bicycle. Indeed, that is the best description of these vehicles — they are submarine motor bikes, driven by small electric motors and steered by fins and rudders. Flat out, they can do fifteen miles an hour — which is usually too fast for comfort under-water. They carry powerful headlights and are fitted with still and movie cameras in case their riders meet anything interesting. Down here, a hundred fathoms deep, only a few faint gleams of indigo-blue light penetrate, even at noon on the clearest days. Most of the time it is completely dark except for the strange, phosphorescent patterns of fish fleeing from their enemies or luring their prey into their gaping mouths.

Let's look more closely at the equipment one of the divers is wearing. Only his hands are exposed to the water — the rest of his body is covered by a thick rubber suit. Don't misunderstand the purpose of this suit — it provides abso-lutely no protection from the surrounding pressure. Indeed, it transmits the whole of that pressure to the diver's body. Its job is purely to insulate him from the bitter cold, for the temperature falls rapidly as you descend into the sea. In the greatest ocean depths, it is always near freezing point — even on the equator. Cold is the mortal enemy of the diver, for it saps his energy, lowers his morale, and makes him use up his air supply much too swiftly. With a suit designed to trap his body heat, a man can swim all day in icy water. Without it, he would be dead in a very few minutes.

Our three explorers are wearing breathing apparatus that looks very much like the Aqua-lungs of today. However, the twin cylinders strapped on their backs are made not of

metal but of Fiberglas which can withstand very much
higher pressures without becoming excessively heavy. (Not
that weight is much of a problem here where the water
buoys everything up.) Those cylinders hold gas so enormously compressed that it is almost as dense as water, and
the gas they contain is not ordinary air. It is a special mixture containing no nitrogen and very little oxygen, designed
for breathing six hundred feet down where normal air would
be a deadly poison.

And here is a strange paradox. If these divers lose their
way in the underwater world and run out of air, they cannot
go up to the surface to breathe. They are only two hundred
yards away from sun and air — a distance they could swim
in a few minutes, or cover with their submarine scooters in
seconds. Yet if they surfaced, they would die horribly from
the bends. It has taken them weeks to become accustomed
to the pressure down here, and it will take more weeks to
reverse the process so that they can return to the upper world.

This is merely one of the problems of life in the deep,
and there are many others. For example, at high pressures
and in these peculiar atmospheres, men's voices change so
much in pitch that they often find it impossible to talk to
each other — the sounds they make are almost meaningless.
This may seem more amusing than serious, but to underwater explorers, good communication is a matter of life and
death. In order to overcome this unexpected difficulty,
some deep sea divers have had to abandon the telephone
and go back to the telegraph key.

Perhaps by this time you are wondering: Is this sort of
thing worth doing in view of the dangers and problems involved? After all, can't we get the same results, and carry
out the same investigations, by sending men down in armored bathyscapes — or even by using underwater TV so

that we can stay on the surface and watch in comfort without
any risk at all?

This is a very good question, but it cannot be answered
until we know more about man's ability to live in the sea.
We can be quite sure that if something is possible, men will
want to do it just to say that it has been done. Look at the
effort that went into climbing Mount Everest. And as far
as diving is concerned, we shall always have in front of us
one amazing example as a perpetual challenge.

For there is a creature, breathing air as we do and drown-
ing if it stays underwater too long, which can descend into
the sea to the incredible depth of three thousand feet —
more than half a mile. And it makes the round trip without
the help of bottled air, relying entirely on the capacity of
its own lungs.

This mightiest of all divers is the sperm whale, hero (or
villain) of Herman Melville's famous novel, *Moby Dick*.
We shall have a good deal more to say about whales later
in this book. What concerns us at the moment is that most
of these great animals don't have to descend very far into
the sea in search of food, as they graze upon the floating
plant and animal life found near the surface. But the sperm
whale is an exception. It has to dive deep for its prey, the
ten-armed giant squid, perhaps the most terrifying of all
the sea's creatures. No one knew how far the sperm whale
could descend until 1932 when the failure of a submarine
cable led to a remarkable discovery. The cable repair ship
— with great difficulty — hauled the broken cable up from
a depth of 3,240 feet, and found a 45 foot sperm whale
hopelessly entangled in it. Perhaps the animal mistook the
cable for the tentacles of a squid. In any event its misfortune
was science's good luck, for there was no other way in which
we could have learned how far these great animals can dive.

Presumably they can go even deeper than this — perhaps as much as a mile down into the ocean.

How do they do it? We'd like to know. It seems quite incredible that an air-breathing mammal fifty or sixty feet long can hold its breath for an hour while taking part in violent battles, and diving so deeply that the pressure on its body increases to a hundred times its normal pressure. When we learn the sperm whale's secret, we may be able to use it ourselves.

There are some other possibilities which today may seem even more farfetched. Sea water contains air, and fish are able to breathe it thanks to their gills — those delicate, fleshy openings on either side of the head. Just as our lungs extract the life-giving oxygen from the air around us, so the gills of fish extract it from their surrounding "atmosphere" of water. Some scientists have suggested that it may one day be possible to make artificial gills so that men could stay underwater indefinitely without having to rely on tanks of compressed air. They might even be grafted into the body by a surgical operation. This sounds a rather repulsive idea, but it need not be painful and a scientist who planned a long period of underwater research might think it worth while. He could always have his gills removed again when he wanted to rejoin land-based society.

You may be surprised to learn that at one time, a few months before you were born, *you* had a set of primitive gills. Every human being, during the nine months in the womb, retraces the story of evolution from sea to land, and at one stage the embryo is almost more fish than animal. It may be possible someday, when medical science has advanced far beyond its present level, to continue development at this stage and to produce men-fish who could live in air or water.

Most people would consider this a perfectly horrible idea worthy of a B-grade monster movie. The result would, in fact, probably look rather like some of the creatures from various Hollywood lagoons. But one day our descendants may have to colonize strange and distant worlds that are covered with ocean and possess little or no dry land. And then they may consider such experiments worth while.

Several years ago one of the world's greatest physiologists, Professor J. B. S. Haldane, told me that he thought it might be possible for men to breathe liquids instead of air if some suitable fluid could be devised to act as a carrier of oxygen. The space-medicine experts are also thinking along these lines, for a man completely immersed in a liquid can withstand accelerations dozens of times greater than the normal force of gravity. By buoying him up, the liquid supports his weight even when it is measured in tons instead of pounds.

If these ideas — that is all they are at the moment — ever bear fruit, they may open up the really deep sea to exploration by men without protective armor. With the lungs full of liquid instead of gas, the problem of resisting the outside pressure would be solved. The water pressure around the diver could be a thousand times greater than normal and it wouldn't matter — he would have the same pressure inside him and the two would cancel out harmlessly. So it is just possible — although very unlikely — that one day men may walk or swim even in the deepest ocean trenches, not merely peer out at them from the security of their thick-walled bathyscapes.

This would be a technical achievement in some ways more difficult than the crossing of space. It is strange to think that we will have explored worlds millions of miles from Earth before we set foot upon parts of our own planet that are only seven miles away.

chapter 4

Ships of Tomorrow

MEN have sailed the surface of the oceans for thousands of years, but the first practical under-sea vessels appeared only a century ago. The submarine was developed entirely for military purposes and not with any idea of scientific or commercial use, although some of the early pioneers did envisage cargo submarines that could travel in the calm water below the reach of the mightiest storms. Nothing came of this idea, nor could it have done so in the days before atomic power.

The submarine has taught us disappointingly little about the sea. The men inside it have been too busy to do much scientific study. There are signs, however, that this is chang-ing. It is now widely realized that the submarine is the only kind of vessel that can explore the icebound Arctic Ocean, and the historic voyage of the U.S.S. *Nautilus* to the North Pole in August, 1958, set the pattern for many expeditions to come. The Russians, however, are the first to fit out an entire submarine as a scientific laboratory. They have at least one vessel engaged in full-time underwater research.

Although the exact figures are secret, the diving limit for today's submarines is about a thousand feet. The number of vessels that can go deeper than this can be counted on the fingers of one hand.

The first of them all was the famous bathysphere, or depth sphere, used by Dr. William Beebe and Otis Barton to descend three thousand feet in 1934. The bathysphere,

DR. BEEBE'S FAMOUS
BATHYSPHERE

however, was not a true ship of the deep. It was a diving chamber lowered by a cable, unable to move under its own power. Peering through its windows, Dr. Beebe was able to see creatures that no human eye had ever seen before. He was the first scientist to enter a world as strange as Mars. His account of his dives, *Half Mile Down*, will always remain one of the greatest classics of marine exploration.

The man who opened up the way to the practical exploration of the greatest ocean depths is that remarkable Swiss scientist, Professor Auguste Piccard, who was also the first man to make a balloon trip into the stratosphere. Piccard's bathyscape, or depth-boat, the first model of which was completed in 1948, is in fact a kind of underwater balloon, able to sink down into the sea and to return to the surface by releasing its ballast. Such a craft, incidentally, was described in detail more than half a century ago by

H. G. Wells, in a short story called "In the Abyss." The important difference between the bathysphere and the bathyscape is that the latter is free to move up and down under its own power, and does not need to be suspended from an enormously heavy and expensive cable — which could easily break and doom the undersea explorers.

Of course, an underwater balloon cannot use gas to lift it, because any gas would be so compressed at great depths that it could provide no buoyancy at all. Six miles down, air would be squeezed denser than water, so that a bubble would not rise, but would sink! Liquids, however, shrink only very slightly under the greatest pressure met in the ocean. So as long as the bathyscape cabin hangs beneath a container of some liquid lighter than water, it can be made to float at any level. The analogy with a balloon still holds good, except for that fact that instead of using a gas lighter than air to support a gondola in the sky, we are using a liquid lighter than water to support one in the sea. The lifting liquid so far used is ordinary gasoline.

To make sure that the bathyscape will sink, ballast in the form of iron shot has to be carried. When the vessel reaches the bottom this can be dropped, and the explorers will float back to the surface. It all sounds very simple — and so it is, in theory — but endless technical problems had to be solved before it could be carried out in practice. You cannot take chances with the enormous pressures that exist at the bottom of the sea, and the entire bathyscape was designed on what is called the fail-safe principle. If anything went wrong, the vessel would come up automatically.

One important difference between the bathyscape and the submarine is that it is unnecessary to design the whole vessel to withstand the tremendous pressure of the depths. Only the small cabin holding the explorers has to be watertight, and with modern engineering techniques and materials, it is not difficult to make a thick-walled metal sphere that would not collapse even at the bottom of the Marianas Trench thirty-six thousand feet down. All the rest of the bathyscape can be built of fairly thin, light metal — even such items as electric motors and batteries do not have to be armored against the pressure. It is necessary only to immerse them in a tank of insulating oil which has an opening into the sea. The oil stops the salt water from short-circuiting the electricity and equalizes the pressure inside and out. Except for the gondola, therefore, the bathyscape does not attempt to fight against the water pressure. It simply accepts it.

At the moment there are only two bathyscapes in existence, both built according to the basic Piccard design. Piccard's achievement has been truly called one of the greatest examples of individual planning, design and construction in the history of science. It is doubtful if we will ever see anything like it again. The French Navy's FNRS-3 had held the depth record of 13,284 feet from 1954 to 1960, when the Italian *Trieste*, purchased by the U. S. Navy, succeeded in reaching the deepest known spot in the ocean. On January 23, 1960, Lieutenant Donald Walsh and Dr. Jacques Piccard, son of the inventor, were the first men to see the bottom of the Marianas Trench, off the Philippines. The *Trieste* reached a depth of 35,780 feet — greater than any that was previously known to exist — and the last terrestrial frontier was thus attained.

The problem of manned exploration of the very greatest ocean deeps is, therefore, already solved. But today's bathyscapes — like all new inventions — have grave disadvantages and will one day look as primitive as the first Wright brothers biplane. Let's consider some of these disadvantages,

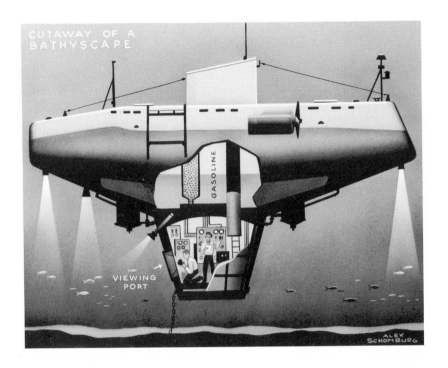

CUTAWAY OF A BATHYSCAPE

GASOLINE

VIEWING PORT

ALEX SCHOMBURG

and the ways in which they may possibly be overcome.

Running a bathyscape is extremely expensive. On each dive, tons of iron shot are needed to take it down, and thousands of gallons of gasoline to balloon it back to the surface. The gasoline is a great nuisance, for it introduces the risk of fire when the bathyscape is on the surface and has often given the handling teams some anxious moments.

There must be a better way of providing buoyancy. All we need, remember, is something lighter than water, something which will not shrink much under the pressures met at the depth to which the bathyscape will dive. It need not be liquid. After all, there are plenty of solids weighing less than water. You may be surprised to know that there are several metals that will float. One that has been suggested for bathyscapes is lithium, used in the so-called hydrogen bomb. Lithium is considerably lighter than water, so solid floats made of it would give plenty of lift and could be built permanently into the structure of the bathyscape.

Although they were fitted with electric motors and propellers, the first bathyscapes could move only very slowly in the horizontal direction. They also had an extremely limited range so they could explore only a small area around the point where they touched the sea bed. Tomorrow's depth ships will need much greater power and speed. This can be provided by the modern storage batteries that have been developed for missile use.

In the next few years, therefore, the manned exploration of the ocean deeps should be well under way. What will we discover down there six or seven miles from the last light of the sun? To repeat the answer many explorers have given, "If we knew what we'd find, we wouldn't bother to go." It may well be true in this case, as it has so often been in the past, that the greatest discoveries are completely unexpected. We can be sure of finding strange living creatures, valuable minerals and ores, and priceless scientific knowledge; some of these possibilities we'll discuss in later chapters. But we might as well be honest and admit right away that the building of deep-diving bathyscapes will be inspired to a large extent by that ancient, unexplained human characteristic which has driven men to the poles and to the top of Mount Everest, and is now driving them to the stars. As long as there is *any* place unvisited or unexplored, men will want to go there, even if there is no particularly good reason for doing so. And when we lose this impulse we will no longer be men — but vegetables.

One class of vessel which is only now coming into existence, and which may teach us even more about the ocean than the depth ships prowling along the sea bed, is the mid-ocean submarine, designed to operate one or two miles down. The tireless Professor Piccard has invented a vessel to do this which he calls the mesoscape (medium or intermediate ship, as opposed to the bathyscape or deep ship). The professor's first craft was an underwater balloon. The one he plans now is an underwater helicopter. It will be a fairly large sphere, much of it made of transparent Plexiglas instead of steel. Unlike the bathyscape gondola, therefore, it will be lighter than water, and the problem will be to make it sink rather than to bring it back to the surface.

A large horizontal propeller, like a helicopter rotor, will pull the mesoscape down into the sea, and other propellers will allow it to move horizontally. The whole machine will be far cheaper to run than the bathyscape, and its Plexiglas walls will give a wonderful view of the deep sea and its creatures. Who would not thrill at the thought of sitting in the middle of the ocean, no longer peering through a narrow porthole, but looking out in all directions from the inside of an almost invisible goldfish bowl? Although in this case, of course, the fish would be on the outside.

Probably you have spotted one of the most attractive features of the mesoscape. If the motor fails, it will automatically rise back to the surface, for it is the tug of the propeller that keeps it down.

Another type of medium-depth vessel has been built by Captain Cousteau and the French Navy Undersea Research Group. This has been humorously christened a "diving saucer" because of its shape, although perhaps "turtle" is a better name. Designed to operate around the thousand-foot mark, it is intended for the exploration of the continental slope in the region which Aqua-lung- and helmet-diver cannot reach.

An interesting idea put forward in the United States by the Reynolds Metals Company, and now being investigated

by the Office of Naval Research, is a project for an aluminum
submarine that will be able to descend about four miles.
The three-man "aluminaut" would be forty-five feet long
and have plates six inches thick. Being much lighter than
the steel bathyscape, it would not need huge buoyancy floats,
but could hover in mid-water like the mesoscape. With a
range of one hundred miles, it could explore a considerable
area before returning to the surface, and could remain submerged for a day or more at a time.

It is worth noting that a submarine that could descend
four miles would be able to reach more than ninety-five per
cent of the ocean bed, for only a very small portion of the
sea is deeper than this. More than half the sea bed, in fact,
lies above the level already reached by the bathyscape, so
there will be only a limited use for vessels that can dive to
the ultimate depths. A submarine that can dive three or
four miles will be able to tackle almost every exploring job
in the sea.

At this moment, billions of dollars are being spent on the
construction of atomic-powered submarines capable of
launching long-range missiles from beneath the sea. The
famous U.S.S. *Nautilus* was the first true underwater vessel
capable of cruising, submerged, at full speed for weeks at a
time. All earlier submarines had to come to the surface at
frequent intervals to take in fresh air or to recharge their
batteries and could carry only limited amounts of fuel. But
the U.S.S. *Nautilus* can extract all the oxygen she needs
from the water around her, and her uranium-powered engines
are completely independent of any atmosphere. It's been said
that she need come up only to let the crew re-enlist.

The spectacular success of the U.S.S. *Nautilus* has, in the
opinion of many, changed the pattern of naval power. The
battleship of the future will be a submarine, if only because

surface ships can be so easily located by radar and destroyed by atomic guided missiles. By contrast, it is extremely difficult to detect a submarine lurking on the sea bed. In fact, at present no way is known of doing so with certainty. The submariners argue that their boats can act as secret launching sites whose position would never be known to an enemy. One cannot help wondering, by the way, what an old-time submarine commander would have thought if you had told him that one day submarines would be able to attack targets more than a thousand miles inland, with weapons traveling three hundred miles above the earth. Imagine a submarine — or indeed any kind of ship — destroying Denver or Chicago! Yet that is now perfectly possible.

There is no doubt that the missile-armed atomic submarine is one of the most terrible weapons ever conceived, but it has limitations which the enthusiasts perhaps overlook. For one thing, it is extremely slow. Today's bombers travel twenty times as fast. When traveling at top speed, it is very noisy and can be detected many miles away by underwater microphones. I'll say more about sound under the sea in the next chapter. And since radio cannot be used underwater, it is out of touch with its base. This is perhaps the most serious disadvantage of all, for swift and reliable communications are essential in wartime.

Navy scientists of every great power are working on the problem of submarine detection, and sooner or later the answer will be found. Just as radar gave us an all-seeing eye in the heavens, so we may invent an underwater eye, or ear, which will probe the sea and reveal all that moves beneath its surface. When this happens — perhaps it already has — the slow-moving submarine will be doomed as a weapon of war.

It may, however, still have very important peacetime uses. As a cargo vessel or freighter, the submarine has several advantages. It can sail below the weather, just as a jet airliner can fly above it. The greatest storms merely ruffle the surface of the sea, and a few dozen feet down there is eternal calm. All submariners claim that theirs is the most comfortable craft in the navy, and are very sorry for their unfortunate comrades being tossed about on the surface.

Another of the submarine's advantages is a little surprising. You might think that a completely submerged vessel would need much more power to push it through the water than does a surface ship of the same size. This, however, is not the case. If you have ever been on a ship moving at high speed, you will have admired the great white V of the bow-wave spreading out on either side. It looks impressive — but it represents a terrible waste of energy. A properly designed submarine slips through the sea without any such disturbance, since when it is submerged it does not produce any waves.

Yet another point in favor of the submarine is that it can take short cuts quite impossible to other vessels. The transpolar voyages of the U.S.S. *Nautilus* and U.S.S. *Skate* are good examples. As the airliners have already shown, hundreds of miles can be cut off some journeys by going over the top of the world. The Arctic — unlike the Antarctic — is one vast sea, but as it is permanently frozen, only submarines can navigate it by traveling beneath the ice.

But how does a submarine know exactly where it is when it has been traveling for days deep down in the sea, perhaps driven off course by powerful currents, and in polar regions where the magnetic compass is useless? The answer, first applied in the German V-2 rocket, is inertial navigation.

Inertia means laziness — the tendency of everything in the universe to resist change and keep on doing whatever it happens to be doing. It makes its appearance when you try to set a stationary object in motion, and when you try to stop something that's already moving.

A very simple experiment will show how this property of all matter can be used to fix position. Take a small but heavy weight and lay it on a smooth, perfectly flat piece of paper — the cover of a glossy magazine will do very well. Now jerk this supporting sheet in some direction, say from left to right. The weight will try to stay still. If it had a pen attached to it, it would trace a line on the paper in the direction of motion and the length of the line would bear a definite relation to the speed of movement.

If you now imagine that this sheet of paper is actually a

map inside a moving ship, then any movement north or south, east or west could be detected and recorded in this way. In fact, a heavy weight resting on the map would try to chart the course of the ship, although friction and other forces would prevent it from doing so.

This is the basic principle of inertial navigation. All the little changes of speed which make up any sort of movement are detected by a very sensitive instrument — far more delicate than the crude arrangement in our example — and are constantly added up in an electronic computer. The whole device is one of the most marvelous inventions of our age, and without it the long-range atomic submarine would soon be lost in the trackless wastes of the sea.

Only time will show whether the possible advantages of submarine merchant ships will outweigh their cost and the problems involved in running them. It seems unlikely that they will ever be used for dry cargoes, which would have to be protected from the surrounding water-pressure, but they might have a future as tugs towing very large liquid loads — oil, for example. Flexible containers rather like underwater

A SUBMARINE TOWS ITS UNDERWATER LOAD

blimps, holding perhaps a hundred thousand tons of oil, may replace the great tankers of today and would be very much cheaper. Since there would be liquid inside and out, they would not have to withstand any pressure, and as they would travel below the reach of the waves they need not be strongly built. At the end of a voyage the empty blimps could be rolled up and shipped back to the oil field for the next trip. Tests have already been carried out successfully with small, liquid-carrying barges made of flexible plastic, christened "dracones," which may lead to larger submarine tankers.

Despite the coming of the airplane, the great highway of the open sea is busier than it has ever been, and in the years to come many strange ships will be sailing on — and under — its restless waters. Since I started writing this book, however, something has happened which may change all our ideas about the shape of ships to come. This is the invention of a totally new type of vessel which can travel on the sea — but is not a boat — and which flies — but is not an airplane. It is the Hovercraft, which floats a few feet above any level surface, whether on land or water.

The Hovercraft is a low, flat vehicle fitted with powerful jet engines which point downward and create an invisible cushion of air — a sort of controlled gale strong enough to support a weight of several tons. Because it is not in contact with land or water, but is surrounded by air on all sides, the Hovercraft has very little friction to overcome and can thus travel at high speeds without requiring much power. At the same time, it is near enough to the earth's surface to use it for support. It cannot rise more than a very few feet into the air without losing its lift.

The interesting thing about the Hovercraft, which seems to combine the advantages of ship and airplane without their disadvantages, is that the bigger it gets, the more efficient it becomes. There would be no great difficulty in making such low-altitude flying boats as big as the *Queen Mary,* yet able to travel several times faster. Plans are now being made for a Hovercraft ferry across the English Channel, which could carry about a thousand passengers and their cars at a hundred miles an hour.

If the Hovercraft principle proves to be sound, it will revolutionize not only the world's shipping but the world's great seaports. For this strange vehicle does not need to be docked; it can skim up any reasonably flat beach and travel on inland for miles, if necessary. Buildings and power lines would be obstacles it couldn't negotiate, but superhighways would suit it very well, except when they entered tunnels. For the first time, we have a vehicle that can travel at high speed with equal ease over land or sea, over deserts or swamps or snow fields.

All these possibilities are opening up an exciting future for the sailors of tomorrow. And how strange it will be if, after so many thousands of years, our ships are about to desert the surface of the sea to travel a few inches above it — or a few hundred feet below.

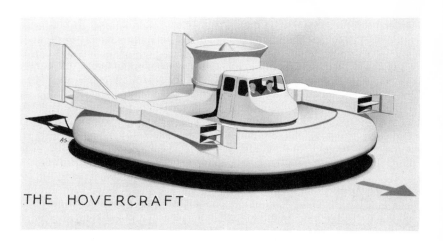

THE HOVERCRAFT

chapter *5*

Voices from the Deep

I⊥T was once thought that the sea was a
silent place, but today we know that this is quite incorrect.
In fact, the creatures of the sea depend upon hearing much
more than they do upon sight. They have to, for most of
the ocean is in complete darkness, and even in the upper
layers where sunlight does penetrate, the water is seldom
clear enough to see more than a few yards. The only way
that most of the sea's inhabitants can avoid obstacles and
enemies, and find their food and their mates, is by means of
sound vibrations.

The sea, therefore, is as noisy as a tropical jungle — although not to our ears, which have evolved to work in air
and are not very efficient underwater. Only when naval
scientists started lowering sensitive microphones into the
sea, in order to detect the engine noises of enemy submarines,
was the idea that fish are dumb thoroughly exploded.

Some fish, indeed, are so talkative that they endangered
the security of the United States. In the spring of 1942 the
network of underwater microphones, or hydrophones, that
formed part of the submarine defense system round Chesa-
peake Bay was put out of action by a most extraordinary
noise. It started every evening, and sounded rather like a
battery of pneumatic drills tearing up the pavement.

The scientists suspected that some variety of fish was
responsible for the din and tested this theory by a very neat
experiment — they let off a small charge of explosive under-

water. At once the noise stopped, but started again a few seconds later when the fish had recovered from their surprise.

It did not take long to find that the animal responsible was a small fish known as the Atlantic croaker, huge schools of which had migrated into the bay. The croaker, like most fish, has an air bladder which allows it to adjust its buoyancy. By increasing the air volume it can ascend, and by decreasing it, it can go down. An Aqua-lunger rises and sinks in exactly the same way, by inhaling or exhaling. The air bladder of the croaker, however, is also modified to act as a tiny drum, and the fish has a muscle which can set its diaphragm vibrating. Some 300 million of these little drums had sabotaged the Navy's elaborate antisubmarine defenses.

At almost the same time, a hydrophone network on the Pacific coast experienced a completely different kind of interference — a loud crackling rather like frying eggs or snapping twigs. This was traced not to a fish but to a species of shrimp with one very large claw. By clicking or snapping its claw, this shrimp can make a noise quite out of proportion to its size. Apparently, the claw acts as a kind of piston, producing a jet of water which scares the shrimp's enemies. The noise is incidental, although it may add to the general effect.

Why the croakers make their drumming is not so clear. Perhaps they are social beasts and their chorus gives them a feeling of togetherness. It may be the underwater equivalent of the chattering of monkeys or the cawing of rooks. Many other fish also produce sounds by means of their air bladders, while some rasp their fins or grate their teeth together. One species, the black drum, has been known to make enough noise to disturb the sleep of crews aboard ships at anchor.

You may well ask what the Navy did about the interference caused by the shrimps and croakers. In the case of the croakers, the electronic experts were able to build sound filters which cut out most of the fish noise but still permitted submarine motors to be heard. This trick wouldn't work with the shrimps, because the noise they made covered the entire band of sound from the lowest to the highest notes and completely jammed the hydrophones. Nevertheless, the Navy was able to use the shrimps to its own advantage by preparing maps of shrimp-infested areas where its submarines could hide, safe from Japanese detecting instruments.

Who would ever have thought that charts of shrimp beds would one day be a top-secret aid to the United States Navy? This is a good example of the way in which purely scientific research can have important and unexpected practical applications. The scientist who prepared these charts — Dr. Martin W. Johnson of the Scripps Institution of Oceanography — was later awarded the prized Agassiz Medal of the National Academy of Sciences for his work.

It is not too difficult to discover what fish is making what noise in shallow water, but in the deep sea the problem is much harder to solve. Microphones have now been lowered several miles down into the sea, and have brought back some weird — indeed, terrifying — sounds. Hideous moans and groans, piercing shrieks, even a noise like rattling chains, have been picked up in the deep Pacific.

Nobody knows what creatures make these strange sounds — these voices from a world as alien as another planet, and almost as unexplored. Here is a vast field for future research which may lead to some unexpected discoveries. On the other hand, it may turn out that the makers of these hideous noises are quite ordinary-looking little fish, not terrible monsters of the deep.

If we can identify the various sea noises, this will be a very useful aid to the fishermen of the future. There is even the possibility that, if we make the right sort of noise and play it back into the sea, we may be able to attract the fish we want to catch. Something of this sort has already been done, as we'll see in chapter seven, with electric impulses.

Although hearing plays such an important part in the life of fish, they possess another sense which is equally valuable to them and which is difficult for us to understand. It is something quite outside our range of experience. If you

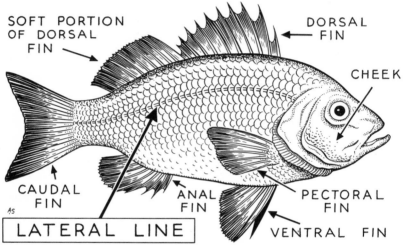

SOFT PORTION OF DORSAL FIN

DORSAL FIN

CHEEK

CAUDAL FIN

LATERAL LINE

ANAL FIN

PECTORAL FIN

VENTRAL FIN

examine a fish carefully, you will notice a thin line running along either side of its body from head to tail. This is called the lateral line, and is an organ for detecting vibrations or pressure waves in the water. Of course, there is no real difference between sound waves and pressure waves — sound waves are pressure waves coming so close together that they make a musical note. However, we cannot sense pressure waves except when they are so powerful that they literally shake us.

But fish, thanks to their lateral line — which acts rather like a kind of ear covering the whole body — can detect very weak and slow vibrations in the water, such as those caused by the movement of other fish. And they can detect obstacles in complete darkness. Indeed, some cave-dwelling and deep-sea fish have lost their eyes altogether, and rely entirely on their lateral lines to "see" their way around. It is quite uncanny to watch some of these blind fish swimming at high speed in a tank — and to notice how they turn in their tracks as soon as they come near the glass, and always at the same distance from it. Probably they feel the wave of their own passage through the water reflected back to them from the obstacle ahead, and so know that there is something in the way. When we understand how these fish perform their feats of sightless navigation, we may learn methods for helping our own blind.

In the case of one marine animal, we have a very good idea of how the "seeing ear" system works. For several years, porpoises or dolphins have been kept at aquariums like Marineland, Florida, and have become great favorites with all visitors. Scientists have been able to study them thoroughly, and have made the amazing discovery that nature has given these animals echo-sounding or sonar systems working on exactly the same principle as those we have now invented for our ships and submarines. The porpoises, however, beat us by several million years.

When it is swimming, a porpoise emits a continuous series of clicks and whistles. These are often quite loud, and can be heard clearly by divers. When a school of porpoises is approaching, you can hear them long before you see them. They sound more like birds than animals. In fact the porpoise whistles are very much like those of a canary.

Experiments carried out with tape recorders and underwater microphones have proved beyond doubt that porpoises listen to the echoes coming back from the sea around them, and have such a wonderfully developed sense of hearing that they can spot even the tiniest obstacles in this manner. They can detect and avoid wires or nets, and in one series of tests it was found that they could swim through complicated underwater obstacle courses — in complete darkness.

Since sound waves travel at almost a mile a second in water, the echoes from an object a foot away come back in about a *ten-thousandth* of a second. Yet porpoises can spot them, so they must have a fantastically developed sense of hearing. The only way that human ears can follow the porpoise's echo-ranging is to slow the whole operation down many times. Just as the slow-motion camera permits us to watch actions far too swift for the human eye, so the tape recorder allows us to hear things happening too quickly for the ear. If porpoise noises are played back on a tape recorder that is slowed down about thirty times, even our sluggish human ears can detect the echo following each chirp the porpoise sends pulsing out into the water.

Porpoises can also make an extraordinary variety of sounds in air. I once had the pleasure of being introduced to some of Marineland's talented performers by their keeper, and they greeted me with barks, grunts, squeals, Bronx cheers and other noises hard to classify. One scientist who has made a special study of the porpoise brain — perhaps the most highly developed in the animal kingdom next to the chimpanzees' — has even suggested that they may be taught to speak. The first aquarium to have a talking porpoise will really draw the crowds.

Whales, which are very closely related to porpoises, also make a great deal of noise. A recording of a school of whales could easily be mistaken for a herd of elephants trumpeting in the jungle. Presumably they, too, use sound waves to guide them through the darkness of the sea. However, it is hardly practical to keep whales in captivity and to study

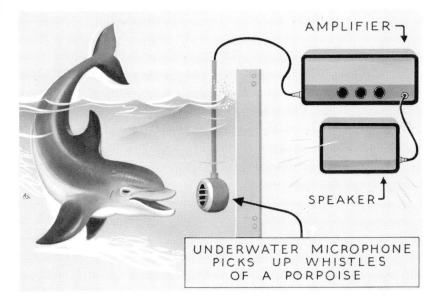

AMPLIFIER

SPEAKER

UNDERWATER MICROPHONE
PICKS UP WHISTLES
OF A PORPOISE

the sounds they produce — although if this could be done, the knowledge gained might be of the very greatest commercial value. The whaling industry — a multimillion dollar business — would be revolutionized if we understood the language of these huge mammals, and could call and herd them like cattle.

During the last twenty years, we have been adding a great deal of man-made noise to the sounds of the sea. The importance of the echo-sounder in determining the depth and shape of the ocean bed has already been mentioned, but soon after sound-ranging equipment came into general use it was discovered that the sea bottom was not the only thing that produced echoes. Schools of fish — and sometimes even single fish — will show up on the echo-sounder record. The trawler captain on his bridge can now watch the fish moving in the sea beneath him, and can judge the best moment when to shoot and lower his nets. As a result, he can catch several times as many fish in a far shorter time.

In the very latest instrument, there is no need for the skipper even to keep his eye on the screen. An electronic detector watches for the fish-echoes, and as soon as they appear, calls for attention through a loud-speaker! To the old-time fishermen, this would indeed seem like magic.

Although the echo-sounder has revealed so many secrets of the sea, it has also brought us face to face with a great mystery. As observations accumulated from the oceans of the world, it was discovered that several hundred feet down in the sea there is a layer, reflecting the waves of the echo-sounder, which moves up and down during the course of the day. At night it approaches the surface, but during the daytime it descends into deeper water — sometimes down to a thousand feet or more. Called the deep scattering layer, this mysterious region of the sea has baffled scientists for more than ten years despite tremendous efforts to solve its mystery. Underwater cameras have been lowered into it, and thousands of electronic flash photographs taken — but all they show are meaningless specks of light.

The deep scattering layer covers most of the world, being absent only in the cold arctic and antarctic seas. It is generally believed to be caused by countless billions of small marine animals which avoid the light — hence their daily up-and-down migration. Quite possibly, this layer is the richest food belt on our entire planet, the sunken prairie in which most of the sea's fish gather their food. One day we may learn to harvest it ourselves — but at the moment we do not even know what it is made of. It is not likely, however, that its secret will escape us much longer, now that more and more men, cameras and other instruments are descending into the sea.

One of the most ingenious uses of sound waves for underwater research is the recently developed "sonic fish tag."

This was invented by scientists of the United States Fish and Wildlife Service and of the Minneapolis-Honeywell Regulator Company, to solve some of the problems of salmon behavior. The fish tag is a tiny sound transmitter in a capsule about two inches long and an inch thick, which can be clipped onto the salmon's dorsal (back) fin without harming the fish or interfering with its movements. Pulses of sound, at a pitch far too high for human ears to detect, are sent out by the tag during the seven hours that its battery lasts, and allow the fish to be tracked underwater at distances of up to half a mile. In this way biologists can study the behavior of salmon near dams — a matter of great importance to sport and commercial fishermen. Before long we may expect many types of fish to be tagged in this way, so that we can follow the movements of individual specimens as they swim in the depths of the ocean. It is as if the fish has a little radio transmitter attached to it, so that, although we cannot see it, we know exactly where it is. When one of these tags is hitched onto a sperm whale, we will at last know just how far down these marvelous divers can descend.

Our scientists and navies are beginning to fill the sea with sound, as already we have filled the space around the earth with our radio programs. And we can make much more noise than any of the sea's own creatures. Our research vessels, for example, are continually letting off explosive charges so that the composition of the ocean bed can be studied from the echoes.

We have just discovered the noises that the fish have been making for millions of years. But what, I wonder, do *they* think of all the bangs and crashes and whistles that we are now pumping into the sea? I cannot help feeling rather sorry for them. There must be lots of fish in the world today suffering from terrible headaches.

chapter 6

The Floating Prairie

SOME of the most important discoveries have been made by asking what seem to be very simple questions — questions so simple, in fact, that they often appear to be stupid. Here is one: What do fish feed on?

Perhaps your first answer is, "Why, smaller fish!" That's partly true — but what do the smaller fish feed on? There must be an end to the line somewhere, when you get down to fish so tiny that there just aren't any smaller ones.

Before we answer this question — and discover how thoroughly the future of mankind may be tied up with it — let's first look at the situation on land. Here, all animal life depends upon plants — chiefly grass, wheat, rice and other cereals. This is true even of meat eaters such as lions, for the creatures they prey upon all live on grass or leaves. When you eat a steak, you are enjoying one of the products of that mobile grass-processing factory, the cow. In a sense, we animals are all parasites on the plant world, for plants alone have the ability to build up the essential chemicals of life from the simplest of all raw materials — water, sunlight, carbon dioxide, and the minerals in the soil.

But where is the grass of the sea upon which fish life must ultimately depend? Only in the last hundred years have we discovered that the sea's upper layers are packed with plants — but plants so tiny that it takes a microscope to show them. All the oceans of the world are covered by an invisible meadow, two hundred feet thick, which provides the basic

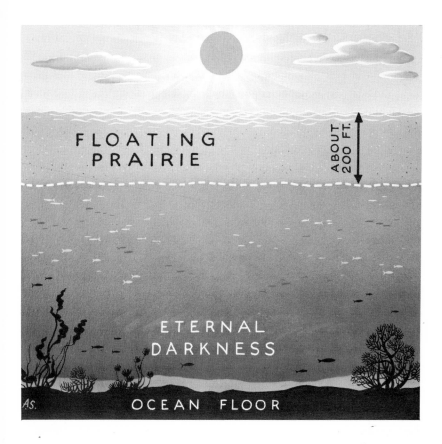

FLOATING PRAIRIE

ABOUT 200 FT.

ETERNAL DARKNESS

AS.

OCEAN FLOOR

food for every creature in the sea from the tiniest shrimp to the mightiest whale.

The sea's plants are small and inconspicuous because they consist of single living cells, and not collections of billions of cells as do the plants (and animals) of the land. Yet despite their minute size, they do exactly the same job as our grasses and cereals and trees. Starting with water, sunlight and the various chemical compounds found in the sea, they combine them together to form the much more complicated substances (such as fats, starches, oils, vitamins) upon which fish and higher animals can feed.

The microscopic plants of the sea do not possess leaves

and stems and flowers. They grow and reproduce without the specialized organs that vegetable life on land has had to evolve. Many of them, however, are as beautiful as any blossom on the face of the earth. They are enclosed in elaborate glass boxes which are shaped in the most fantastic designs. Some are like the glass ornaments hung on Christmas trees, but much more intricately shaped. As one naturalist has described it, "under the microscope these little plants — few of them bigger than a speck of dust — glitter like crystal caskets filled with jewels." Their glassy skeletons are covered with spikes and spines. Some form perforated spheres one inside the other, like those that Chinese craftsmen carve from ivory. It is a pity that they are so small that few people have ever seen them, for they are among the greatest wonders of the living world.

These little plants are eaten by animals scarcely larger than themselves, and the whole plant-animal mixture forms a vast layer of living soup in the upper levels of the oceans. Sometimes it is so dense that it changes the color of the sea, staining it green or brown. The name, plankton, has been given to these creatures; it comes from a Greek word that means "wandering" or "drifting," since these tiny plants and animals cannot move under their own power but float wherever the currents take them. The word, planet, has the same origin, for the planets drift against the background of the fixed stars.

And so here we have the beginning of what has been called the food chain of the sea. This is the material on which the smallest fish feed. The tiny plants in the plankton are the "grass" of the sea upon which all other marine life depends. When you eat fish, you are eating these sea plants at third- or fourth-hand, at the end of a chain which may be something like the following —

        plankton plant is
            eaten by plankton animal which is
                eaten by herring which is
                    eaten by tuna which is
                        eaten by man

Sometimes, however, the food chain is much shorter. In the waters around the Antarctic continent live countless billions of little shrimplike creatures about two inches long, known as krill — or, to give them their scientific name, Euphausiidae. These feed directly on the plankton plants, straining them from the water by tiny bristles along their forelegs. And they in turn are eaten by the greatest of all animals, the whales, which plough through the acres of floating krill, gulping down several tons a day. As a result, we have this extremely short food chain —

        plankton plant is
            eaten by krill which is
                eaten by whale

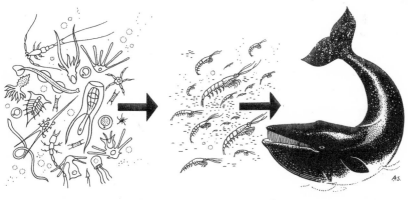

PLANKTON *to* KRILL *to* WHALE

In just two steps, therefore, we get from plants a hundredth of an inch long to animals a hundred feet long. The link is a two-inch shrimp!

Now, all this is very important to us when we consider how much of our food comes from the sea, and how much more we must win from it in the future. So let's look a little more closely at these tiny drifting plants, so small that tens of thousands may be found in a single pint of sea water. Without them there would be no fish, no whales. Where they flourish, so do the larger animals of the sea, and where they are rare the sea is a desert.

You may be surprised to learn that the sea does have deserts — although they are not as barren as those of the land — and also that it has seasons as well. Spring and summer, autumn and winter, come to the sea as they do to the land, and the plants of the ocean respond to them as does the more familiar vegetation of the continents.

All plants depend upon sunlight. They cannot grow in darkness. Now, light can penetrate only a few hundred feet into water before it is absorbed. Most of the sea is in eternal night. It follows, therefore, that *all* the sea's plant life must grow in the upper layers where it can feast upon the rays of the sun. The food eaten by all the fish in the oceans comes ultimately from the sun-drenched couple of hundred feet near the surface — a mere skin on the top of the sea.

Because of their need for light, you might expect that the plants of the sea are more numerous in summer than in winter — when the sun is low and its weak rays do not penetrate far into the water — and that the richest of all the ocean meadows flourish in the sunny tropics. To some extent, this is true, but it is not as simple as this. In nature, it very seldom is. In fact, it turns out that the emptiest regions of the sea are almost on the equator, and the most fertile lie close to the barren ice fields of the Antarctic! This, of course, is almost the exact opposite of the state of affairs on land.

The explanation of this paradox is that plants need more than sunlight to live on. They must have water and food in the form of a wide variety of chemicals containing carbon, nitrogen, phosphorus, oxygen — to mention only the most important elements. Well, there is no shortage of water in the sea, but what about the other materials — the fertilizers, as it were, of the plankton crops?

It is these, the basic chemicals of life, which limit the fertility of the sea. When the plants have consumed them all, no more can grow. They have used up all the nourishment in the ocean — at least, in the layers which they can reach.

This actually happens in the spring and summer, in many areas of the sea. The plankton plants flourish so luxuriantly that they exhaust the chemicals they require for their growth. This, in turn, sets a limit to the fish population — and to the hauls the fishermen bring home to port.

Despite this limiting factor, an acre of sea produces, on the average, more food than an acre of land — and, of course, there is so much more of it. Indeed, it has been estimated that nine-tenths of the world's vegetation is in the sea, and only one-tenth on land. The total tonnage of plant life in the oceans is enormous. Scientists have calculated that the sea produces something like a hundred *billion* (that's 100,000,000,000) tons of living matter every year. The entire human race, to give you some basis of comparison, weighs only about a hundred million tons, or a thousandth of this gigantic figure. We wouldn't make much of a splash if we were all thrown into the sea.

We're more interested, however, in the amount of fish

the oceans produce, than in the amount of vegetation that
grows there. Although any figure can only be a very rough
estimate, it has been calculated that each year the sea produces about a billion tons of fish. We manage to catch
about one-thirtieth of this annual crop. The old saying that
there are plenty more fish in the sea than ever came out of
it is certainly true. But there could be very many more than
there are, if there were enough plankton to support them.
It's of the greatest practical importance, therefore, to find if
there is any way of increasing the fertility of the sea. So
let's look a little more closely at the reasons why some parts
of the ocean are desert while others are covered with a thick
soup of floating plankton.

Even the tiniest and simplest living creatures are vastly
more complicated than an automobile, and contain thousands
of times as many parts. Now the finest automobile can be
put completely out of action if some small but vital bit of
the machinery is missing. For example, consider the spark
plugs. If your car were weighed with them in, and then with
them out, you'd never notice the difference. But you'd notice
it soon enough when you pressed the starter button. Small
though they are — even negligible compared with its total
weight — the spark plugs are essential to the operation of
the car. You may have everything else, including a full tank
of gas, but without plugs all this machinery might just as
well be a pile of junk.

In the same way, if a single vital chemical is missing in
the sea, no plants can grow. They may have all the sunlight,
all the carbon, all the nitrogen, all the sulphur, all the calcium
they need, but nothing will happen if, for example, there's
no phosphorus. Huge areas of the ocean can be a virtual
desert for lack of one substance which may be needed only
in the most minute quantities.

The element, phosphorus, is such a substance — both on land and sea. It is very rare in sea water, and has been truly called "life's bottleneck." The sea's plants and animals don't need much of it — there's only a couple of pounds of phosphorus in a ton of plankton — but when it's all used up, nothing more can grow. It's as if the automobile production line has run out of spark plugs.

Phosphorus is not the only essential material needed by the plant life of the sea, by any means. There are dozens — perhaps hundreds — of other elements and compounds without which plankton growth is stunted or even impossible. But phosphorus is perhaps the most critical of the sea's nourishing substances — or nutrients — and the one that gives out first, so we'll concentrate on it. Most of the things we say about phosphorus will be true of the other essential substances.

You will remember that the plants of the sea can flourish only in the upper two hundred feet where sunlight penetrates. This is merely a thin film on the surface of the sea, and down in the deeper waters — particularly near the very bottom — there are enormous quantities of the life-giving chemicals beyond the reach of the plants that could use them. Fortunately, these deep waters are stirred up by currents which bring some of their priceless mineral wealth — far more valuable than gold, which nobody can eat — welling up to the surface. If this did not happen, all the sea's nutrients would eventually sink down to the bottom, and life in the ocean would die out.

This "stirring up" of the sea happens on a large scale in the Antarctic, when cold water drains from the great ice fields and, being heavier than the surface waters which are warmed by the sun, sinks to the bottom. The currents thus produced on the ocean bed, far from the light of day in a region never seen by man, help to feed millions of people, and one day will feed millions more. For as they creep along the sea bed they push aside the richly laden water already there, and start it moving up to the surface. And here, in the long days of the Antarctic spring and summer, it nourishes the densest fields of plankton in the world, which in turn support countless schools of fish and vast herds of whales.

Much the same thing happens in the cold northern waters of Labrador and Newfoundland, which explains why the world's greatest fishing grounds are here. And it explains why the warm, sunlit seas of the equator are relatively barren. The chemicals that could fertilize them are trapped in the depths, unable to force their way past the barrier of warm, light surface water.

This, in very rough outline, is the pattern of food production in the sea. There is never any lack of water, but unless we have the right combination of sunlight and minerals, no plants will grow.

On land, of course, the farmer meets the same problem. He tries to overcome it by using manure and artificial fertilizers. So the suggestion has often been made that one day we may be able to fertilize the sea — or at least small portions of it.

When one looks at the enormous — the inconceivable — amount of water in the world's oceans, the idea that man could do anything to alter its composition seems fantastic. If you like to have it in figures, the total weight of the sea comes to more than a million, million, million — 1,000,000,000,000,000,000 — tons. All the ores and minerals that the human race has ever mined, since the beginning of history, would make no noticeable change in this immense body of water were they dumped into it.

MINERAL RICH
WATERS
PUSHED UPWARDS
BY CURRENTS

COLD WATER

SEA BED

THE "STIRRING UP" OF THE SEA

Luckily, the situation isn't quite as bad as this. The fertilizers that could make the deserts of the sea burst into life are already in the oceans, and there is no need to add more. It's just that they are in the wrong place, two or three miles down. If we could stir them up, as the cold polar currents do, that would do the trick.

There are several ways in which this might be possible. One interesting idea is to use a coral atoll — one of the circular lagoons so common in the Pacific — and to pump fertilizing water into it from the deep ocean only a few miles away. Atolls are the peaks of submerged mountains, usually springing from great ocean depths. With a little extra engineering, some of them could be turned into enclosed lakes, so that the enriched water would be trapped inside the wall of coral and would not be lost again in the open sea.

Another suggestion, which I put forward some years ago in *The Deep Range,* a novel about whale ranching (see Chapter 8), was that nuclear reactors might be lowered to the sea bed. These are the furnaces which provide the heat that drives our atomic submarines and power stations. It requires a great deal of complicated machinery — boilers, turbines and so forth — to convert this heat into electricity, but here is a way in which we could use atomic heat very simply and directly. Warming the deep ocean water would start it rising, carrying its load of life-bearing fertilizers with it. We would have created a huge fountain on the bottom of the sea, sweeping its riches up to the surface. As far as the health and happiness of mankind are concerned, this might well be one of the most rewarding of all the applications of atomic energy.

One day, perhaps not so very far in the future, we will be constructing dams in the sea and opening vast new waterways from one ocean to another. This may be part of a deliberate attempt to alter the world's climate by changing the pattern of ocean currents, but it will do even more than that. The hidden streams that sweep the fertilizing chemicals up from the depths will move into new courses, and the fish will move with them. It is vital, therefore, that before we attempt experiments of this kind we think of all their possible consequences, for even small changes in the movement of ocean waters can have tremendously important and perhaps undesirable results.

To sum up, then, we have seen how the plants of the "floating prairie" support all life in the sea, and how they, in turn, depend for their existence upon sunlight and minerals, just as do the more familiar plants of the land. This is a matter of interest not only to scientists, but also to the whole human race, for already about a third of our meat comes from the sea. Indeed, in many countries fish is the only protein which most people ever have a chance of eating.

Near the beginning of Melville's *Moby Dick* there is a quotation from an earlier book about Nantucket which reads as follows: "In the year 1690, some persons were on a high hill observing the whales spouting and sporting with each other, when one observed, 'There,' pointing to the sea, 'is a green pasture where our children's grandchildren will go for bread'."

The unknown person who made that remark, more than two and a half centuries ago, was a true prophet. We have seen how this "green pasture" grows. Now let us see how it will be harvested.

chapter 7

The Harvest of the Sea

ALMOST half the people in the world are not properly fed, and perhaps a third of the human race knows actual hunger. Yet the population of the earth is increasing by about a hundred thousand *every day*. It is as if, each twenty-four hours, a new city winked suddenly into existence. One of the greatest problems facing mankind, therefore, is that of finding more food. Starvation is a bigger peril than the H-bomb, when you take the long view.

There are still possibilities for increasing food production on the land; deserts can be reclaimed, forests cleared, poor soils fertilized. But we can see an end to this process, for there is only a limited amount of land, and some of it — the Antarctic for example — may never be cultivated. It is now generally agreed that for most of our new food resources, we must turn to the sea.

Every year the world produces about fifty million tons of meat. This is not enough even for today's population. At the same time, some thirty million tons of fish are taken from the sea. The annual crop of fish in all the oceans, however, is estimated at a *billion* tons. For all our efforts, therefore, we catch less than one fish in thirty from the sea's annual production.

But before we talk about increasing our catches, we must remember that in some parts of the world — the North Sea, for example — we are already taking so many fish that the catches are decreasing. Like a greedy farmer who is exhausting his land, we have been taking more than the sea can yield — a process bound to lead to disaster. So we have to improve our existing fishing grounds, or find new ones elsewhere.

If you look at a map of the world — or better still, a globe — you will see that most of the sea is in the Southern Hemisphere, below the equator. Yet practically all our fish — ninety-eight per cent of it — comes from northern latitudes. Only two fish out of every hundred are caught in the Southern Hemisphere despite the fact that there's more sea there. So here are enormous reserves almost untouched by man. Clearly, it's high time we did something about them.

One big difficulty is transportation — a fish caught in the Antarctic is perhaps ten thousand miles away from the customer. It's not surprising, therefore, that most fishermen stick to waters nearer home. Only the whalers have found it worth while to go to the far south, to the very edge of the great ice barrier around the last unexplored continent. Before long, other fishing fleets may have to do the same. This means there will have to be great refrigeration plants to bring the catch back across the hot tropical seas, or else canning and fish-processing factories in the Antarctic. All this will cost a good deal of money, but it doesn't require any new scientific inventions or discoveries — merely organization and capital.

The greatest advances, however, must come from the application of science, and since the end of the war the fishing industry has been transformed by two inventions which at first sight would seem to have nothing to do with man's ancient occupation of gaining food from the sea. One has already been mentioned. It is the use of sound waves to probe the underwater world. Sonar or echo-ranging equipment was developed to a very high degree of accuracy during the war in order to detect submarines. It works equally well on fish, and all modern trawlers and fishing boats are fitted with it. A trawler captain without his ultrasonic fish-finder now feels like a blind man who has lost his stick. Indeed, many skippers head straight back to port if their echo-sounders break down.

The second great invention that has made the life of the fishermen easier is nylon. For literally thousands of years, nets of rope and twine have been cast into the sea to catch fish. They get torn easily, and rot so quickly that few last more than one season. Now, within the incredibly short time of ten years, the nets that have been used since the beginning of history have become obsolete and are being replaced all over the world. When you consider that fishermen are most conservative, this is something of a miracle.

The new nets of nylon, Dacron and other synthetic materials are stronger, do not rot, and because the fish cannot spot them easily — some are almost invisible in the water — they bring in bigger catches. It is hard for most of us to realize what this can mean to native fishermen who have to rely on the sea for their very existence, and who have been using the same primitive methods for thousands of years. Indian fishermen working from simple log rafts with the new nylon nets have been able to multiply their catches by ten. In some parts of Africa, such as the Belgian Congo, nets made of natural fibers have become extinct almost overnight. Only synthetic nets are now being used. It seems unlikely that any technical change, affecting so many ancient traditions, has ever before spread so quickly to the remotest corners of the world.

But there are other ways of catching fish besides the ancient net or line techniques, and some of them have made considerable progress during the last ten years. Perhaps the most promising — and certainly the easiest as far as the fisherman is concerned — has been developed by the Russians since the war and is widely used in the Caspian Sea. The idea is simplicity itself. You lower a large pipe into the sea and pump the fish into the ship. When your hold is full, you sail for port.

This is really push-button fishing, and takes all the hard work out of the business. Moreover, it results in bigger catches and requires smaller crews. So why doesn't everybody use it?

Well, at the moment it's limited to sardine-sized fish which gather in tightly packed schools, and of course it requires powerful and expensive pumps. And there's another problem: How do you persuade the fish to come near enough to the nozzle of the pump to be sucked into the tube?

The Russians do it by means of powerful underwater lights. Just as moths and night-flying insects are attracted to lights, so many kinds of fish show the same type of behavior. This fact has long been known and applied by fishermen. In the Mediterranean, for example, small boats fitted with kerosene or gas pressure lamps — above the water, of course — have been used for many years to lure fish into the nets. There is a well-known painting by Picasso in the Museum of Modern Art in New York called "Night Fishing at Antibes" showing fishermen using spears to catch fish which their lights have attracted to the surface. However, you would hardly guess this unless you knew beforehand what the picture was about.

The Russians have brought this old idea up to date with their pump ships. An underwater light near the nozzle attracts the fish, bringing them close enough for the suction

SUCTION-PIPE
FISHING

to take over. Before they realize what's happening, they're safely in the hold.

The Japanese have been using underwater lights in a somewhat different way. They employ a long string of lamps to lead fish into their nets which hang in shallow water not far from the shore. Soon after sunset, the fishermen switch on all the lights, which are arranged in a line leading out to sea and ending inside the net. They wait for the fish to gather, then start switching off the lights one by one, beginning at the end farthest from the net. The fish, therefore, travel along the line, following the glow moving through the water — until they end up inside the net.

Twice as many fish can be caught this way as without lights, and the beauty of the system is that lights can be switched automatically while the fishermen sleep soundly at home. In the morning they can simply go down to the beach and count their catch.

It seems obvious that there are great possibilities for the future, when we discover what fish are attracted by lights, and what colors and intensities are the best to use. Some marine animals are repelled by light, but this can be equally useful, as lights could be used to scare fish into nets or pump nozzles.

On a small scale, I once saw a striking example of the way in which underwater lights can attract the creatures of the sea. I was diving at night in the Indian Ocean, using a powerful electric flashlight to see my way around in the pitch-black submarine world. Within seconds of switching on the beam, it began to fill with tiny, rapidly moving specks, as millions of small shrimplike creatures were attracted by the glare. The cloud in the beam grew thicker and thicker until it seemed almost solid, and there was a steady patter, like hail on a roof, as countless little animals hurled them-

selves against the lens. In a very short time they formed
such an underwater fog that it was impossible to see anything, and I had to switch off the light and wait for them
to disperse.

It is very simple to use underwater lights to attract fish,
and the gear needed can easily be made by the fishermen,
themselves, but it has one serious limitation. Even in the
clearest water, light does not penetrate very far. A few
dozen feet — sometimes much less — is the greatest distance
from which fish could see the lamps intended to attract them.
What we would like is something with much more range —
some "fish call" which could bring everything within several
hundred yards flocking into the nets.

There are two obvious possibilities — sound and electricity. Let's consider sound first.

That fish make — and hear — a wide variety of noises has
already been explained. This is still a very recent discovery
which has opened up a vast and fascinating field of research.
We would like to know which fish make what noises, and
why. It is going to take us many years to learn the language
of the sea, but when we have done so, the results may be
of the greatest practical importance. If we can record, and
play back into the sea, noises which attract — or frighten —
particular varieties of fish, then we will have given the
fishermen a powerful new weapon. Sound travels very well
underwater, and a range of several miles would be possible
even with quite low-powered equipment.

Underwater hunters have known for a long time that
some fish are attracted by vibrations. This has been proved
over and over again, in the case of sharks, by a very simple
experiment. If you spear a fish in waters where sharks
abound, they will often arrive on the scene within seconds
and start circling in the distance. The only signal that could

possibly have brought them racing from hundreds of yards away must have been some noise or vibration emitted by the injured fish. Sight and scent can have nothing to do with it — in fact, a shark will often take a considerable time to find a bleeding fish in perfectly clear water — if it is dead and therefore completely motionless. But the soundless shrieks of an injured fish will bring the sharks racing in like an express.

Soon after the war, Dr. Hans Hass, the famous Austrian pioneer of underwater exploration, took out world patents on a scheme for attracting fish by sound. He made some inconclusive experiments in the Red Sea under very difficult conditions (described in his fascinating book *We Come From the Sea*), but otherwise no one else seems to have done much work along these lines. This is a pity, for we may be missing some really big opportunities.

On the other hand, perhaps sound is already being used successfully in the sea — but the people employing it are saying as little as possible because they want to keep the idea to themselves. Some years ago it was reported that whales showed signs of fright when the ships hunting them switched on their echo-sounders and started sweeping the water with ultrasonic beams. The whales could pick up the vibrations — too high-pitched for human ears — and obviously didn't like them at all. A whale caught in a beam of underwater sound turns its body so that it lies along the beam, apparently because in this position it feels the least discomfort. This means, of course, that it is forced to swim in a fixed direction, and Norwegian whalers are said to have used this idea to drive the great animals toward the catching ships.

Although fishing by sound has hardly started, fishing by electricity has been employed successfully for many years. The Germans and the Japanese are the pioneers in this field.

Patents were taken out for electrical fishing in Japan as long ago as 1895, and practical experiments started in the 1920's.

Probably you have seen the experiment in physics where iron filings are shaken on a piece of paper over a magnet, and line themselves up pointing toward the magnet's poles. Fish behave in much the same way in an electric field. If two metal plates are lowered into water, one connected to each terminal of a direct current supply, fish will turn with their heads toward the positive plate. If the current is powerful enough, they will swim toward it, and in very powerful fields they will be stunned or even killed outright.

In fresh water this works extremely well, and it needs only a small amount of power to bring fish swimming helplessly into the waiting nets. Among the advantages of electro-fishing is the fact that it will drag fish out of rocks or weeds where they cannot be caught in any other way. Moreover, it affects large fish much more strongly than the little ones. Because they are bigger, they pick up more electricity. This is fine from the fisherman's point of view, as he doesn't want to bother about the little fellows, but would rather wait until they grow up. Finally, electro-fishing does not harm the fish. They will recover completely (unless the field is too strong) and any not wanted can be thrown back into the water none the worse, except for their fright.

So successful is this kind of fishing in some streams and lakes that enterprising poachers have been taking it up, to the fury of anglers who consider it not at all sporting. It is said that in Scotland quite a few trout streams have been raided in this way, usually under cover of darkness. It would serve them both right if one of the electrical poachers caught one of the skin-diving poachers who also work in the same rivers.

Electro-fishing sounds too good to be true, and in fact it has one very big drawback which has severely limited its use in the open sea. The fresh water of rivers and lakes is a bad conductor of electricity, so it takes very little power to set up a strong electric field — even batteries will do it. But the salt water of the sea is a good conductor — hundreds of times better than fresh water — so it will carry heavy electric currents. It needs a lot of power, therefore, to set up an electric field, and batteries are useless. Even with powerful generators it is impossible to attract fish in the open sea from distances of more than twenty or thirty feet.

Scientists have tried to increase the range by using short, sharp pulses, storing up electrical energy and then letting it out in one big bang. Another idea, which has been tried successfully, is to fire an electrified buoy into a school of fish by means of a special gun. The fish cannot escape from the electric field around the buoy, and a boat fitted with a suction hose steams up and pumps them in.

Because of its limited range, the electrical method seems best, not so much for attracting fish, but for preventing them from running away. The United States Fish and Wildlife Service demonstrated this with the research vessel *John N. Cobb* a few years ago, when underwater lights, electricity, and suction pumps were all combined in what must have been the most scientific fishing the world has yet seen. The fish were attracted to the ship by lights, held there by electricity, and pumped aboard through a hose — at rates up to twenty a second!

One use of electricity which has been proved in actual practice — although it is not yet as widely used as it might be — is for the quick killing of large, active fish which might escape even when they are hooked or netted. The tuna is a good example. These splendid fish may weigh almost half a ton, and sometimes nine out of ten get free again after they are hooked. However, if the hook is connected to an electric generator, the fish is stunned immediately when it takes the bait, and can be hauled aboard without difficulty. Not only can the fishermen multiply their catches in this way, but they are spared hours of exhausting labor.

Perhaps it is in whaling that electricity can play its greatest part. No one worries much about the feelings of fish, whose sensitivity to pain is probably quite low; indeed, they may not experience pain as we know it. But whales are warm-blooded, intelligent, and peaceful mammals, grazing harmlessly like cattle on the pastures of the sea, with feelings and emotions which we can share. For centuries they have been hunted with spears and lances, and since the invention of the harpoon gun some ninety years ago, more than a *million* of these great animals have been slaughtered. The harpoon gun, exploding in the body of the whale, seldom kills its victim instantly, and wounded whales have been known to tow ships for several hours.

What a public outcry there would be if any land animals — deer, for example — were hunted by men firing explosive harpoons from jeeps! Yet whales are more intelligent than deer, and just as sensitive to pain. It has been said that few men would have strong enough nerves to bear the last moments of a harpooned whale if the great animal had vocal chords that could express its sufferings.

A good deal of effort, not entirely for humanitarian reasons, has gone into the development of electric harpoons, and experiments carried out in the Antarctic in 1949 gave very promising results. When the whale is hit, and the current switched on, the animal dies without a struggle in a matter of seconds. This makes catching far easier — there is no need to hit a vital spot, since the electric shock, not a bomb in the harpoon head, does the killing. And because the whale does not exhaust itself in efforts to escape its flesh is in a better and less damaged condition than if the animal were caught by an explosive harpoon. So the electric harpoon makes sense both to the whale hunters and to those who are interested in avoiding unnecessary suffering. Let us hope that explosive harpoons will soon become obsolete, if not prohibited, when the electric harpoon has finally been perfected.

There is another way of catching marine animals which has been used on a small scale and which is worth mentioning because of its interest, although it does not seem likely that it offers much in the way of future possibilities. This is the employment of other animals as hunters. Perhaps the best-known examples of this are the trained cormorants that the Chinese have used for centuries to catch fish. The birds have rings fastened around their necks so that they can swallow only the smallest fish. Large ones they have to hand over to their masters.

Otters have also been employed as underwater hunters in some parts of the world, but the most ingenious use of animals occurs in the Pacific, where one fish has been used as a kind of guided weapon. The remora, or suckerfish, has a suction pad on the top of its head that allows it to grip onto any smooth surface with great power. Most large sharks and rays have at least one of these submarine hitchhikers hanging onto them. When the natives of New Guinea or Northern Australia go out turtle hunting in their canoes, they tie a remora onto a rope and play it out when they get near a turtle. The remora heads toward the turtle, hoping to get a free ride, and fastens onto the shell. Then the hunters slowly pull in the rope. In this manner turtles weighing a couple of hundred pounds can be landed — and if the fishing expedition is unsuccessful, one can always eat the remora.

All these are small-scale efforts, used by a few fishermen to catch a few fish. One day, however, it may be worth while to train more intelligent and more powerful animal hunters to herd large schools of fish in much the same way that dogs are used to drive sheep. Does this seem fantastic? So it did to me until I discovered that it had actually happened — and more than a hundred years ago. Here is a quotation from an article written by a naturalist in 1856, describing the hunting methods of the Australian aborigines along the Queensland coast:

> Some of the natives may constantly be found during the warmer months fishing for mullet . . . in this pursuit they are assisted in a most wonderful manner by the porpoises. It seems that from time immemorial a sort of understanding has existed between the blacks and the porpoises for their mutual advantage, and the former pretend to know all the porpoises about the spot, and even have names for them.

> The beach here consists of shelving sand, and near the shore are small hillocks of sand, on which the blacks sit, watching for the appearance of a shoal of mullet. On seeing a shoal, several of the men run down, and with their spears make a peculiar splashing in the water.

> Whether the porpoises really understand this as a signal, or think it is the fish, it is difficult to determine, but the result is always the same; they at once come in towards the shore, driving the mullet before them. As they near the edge, a number of the blacks with spears and hand-nets quickly divide to the right and left, and dash into the water. The porpoises being outside the shoal, numbers of the fish are secured before they can break away. In the scene of apparent confusion that takes place, the blacks and porpoises are seen splashing about close to each other. So fearless are the latter

that strangers, who have expressed doubts as to their tameness, have often been shown that they will take a fish from the end of a spear, when held out to them.

In Victorian days a tale like this must have been hard to believe. But we have seen tame porpoises performing, and know how intelligent and cooperative they can be, so there is no reason at all to doubt the complete accuracy of this story.

It has also been reported that the fierce killer whales — which are really giant porpoises — have been known to drive larger whales toward the catching ships, apparently in the hope of sharing the spoils when the human hunters have saved them the trouble of a kill. Although this is a little hard to credit, there is nothing impossible about it. The great baleen (plankton-eating) whales are so terrified of their cannibal cousins that they will even hurl themselves onto land in their frantic efforts to escape.

So there are at least two swift and powerful animals in the sea — mammals like us — which could be trained to herd fish or other marine creatures. Porpoises and killer whales are both extremely intelligent — much more so than the sheep dogs men have employed for centuries — and as they use sound for communication, we should be able to direct them through underwater loud-speakers.

Would this be worth doing? Probably not. It is usually easier to work with machines than with animals. Yet it seems a pity not to take advantage, to the benefit of both parties, of the keen brains and swift bodies that already inhabit the sea. It would at least be interesting to try the experiment.

chapter 8

The Last Roundup

IN the sea man is still a hunter, however scientific the methods he uses. He has to locate his prey in the vast expanses of the ocean. The schools of fish and herds of whales he chases are completely wild and beyond his control, free to travel where they will.

How different it is on land! The whole story of civilization has been bound up with the change from hunting to agriculture. Before he discovered how to sow and reap crops, and to domesticate such animals as cows, sheep and goats, man was a homeless wanderer on the face of the earth. Not until the invention of farming, perhaps twenty thousand years ago, could he stay in one place and establish villages, towns, and, later, cities.

In terms of food production, tilling the soil and rearing farm animals is scores of times more efficient than hunting. For the most dramatic proof of this, consider what has happened in North America during the last four centuries. At the beginning of that time the great prairies supported a few million Indians and the mighty herds of bison which they hunted for meat and hides. Today, the bison are gone. But the miles of grain sprouting from the soil over which they once roamed help to feed hundreds of millions of people in many lands.

With such examples behind us, and a mounting food shortage looming up ahead, it is not surprising that scientists have asked one another, "Is there any way in which we can farm the sea, and thus improve its productivity as we have done on land?" The answer to this question may well determine the future of the human race — or even decide whether it has a future.

There are two basic types of farming — growing crops, and rearing animals. The first is, of course, more fundamental, since you have to have some kind of crop — if only grass — to feed your herds. But so far, the harvesting of marine plants has scarcely been attempted. Except for certain seaweeds, all the food that man has taken from the ocean has been the flesh and oil of fish, whales or other animals. So we will start with these familiar products of our sea hunting and consider whether we may one day hope to farm them.

You may be surprised to learn that the Chinese and other Eastern peoples have been running "fish farms" for centuries. These are small ponds or lakes which are kept properly tended and fertilized, and stocked with fish which grow to maturity and are then caught. Doing the same sort of thing in the open sea obviously presents great problems, and even if it could be done at all, would only be worth while in exceptional circumstances.

For example, we might decide to enrich the plankton crop in some suitable region, by the methods suggested in chapter six, and then catch the fish that had fattened themselves on it. Something of this sort was tried during the war, when fertilizing chemicals were dumped into a Scottish loch, and, as a result, the fish grew at several times their normal rate. If such an experiment were carried out in the sea, we would wish to make sure that the fish we fattened did not swim away before they could be caught. So we might enclose areas of the ocean, not by actual nets, but by invisible fences of sound or electricity — or by curtains of bubbles which look

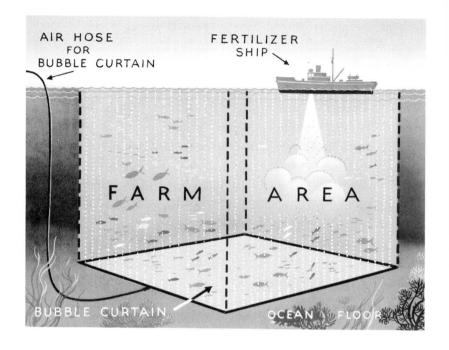

AIR HOSE FOR BUBBLE CURTAIN   FERTILIZER SHIP

FARM   AREA

BUBBLE CURTAIN   OCEAN FLOOR

like solid walls to fish. In this way, we could also keep out
predatory animals such as sharks, which would attack our
"flocks." All this could be done. Only large-scale tests will
show if it is worth doing, or if, on the other hand, the cost
will be so great that we won't be able to afford fish raised
on sea farms.

There are many large bays and partly landlocked seas
where experiments of this kind will certainly be carried out
sooner or later. But the open ocean seems rather too big a
place for us to cultivate on any scale, at least in the near
future. It may, in fact, never be worth while, for the shallow
seas over the continental shelves are many times more pro-
ductive in food than the open ocean. When all the dry land
has been tamed and cultivated, the deep ocean may still
remain utterly savage — the last wilderness in the world.

Although many kinds of fish, like the swift herrings, tunas, and jacks, spend all their lives swimming in the open sea, other less active fish make their homes in caves and wrecks which provide them with shelter and protection. Every skin-diver knows how quickly a wreck becomes packed with inhabitants of all shapes and sizes. In fact, I have often wondered how some fish managed to solve their housing problems in the days before there were any wrecks. Although it may sound somewhat laughable to design houses for fish, this is just what is happening now at the Monaco Oceanographic Museum, founded in 1910 by the great sailor-scientist Prince Albert I.

Here, a small undersea town, complete with streets and even street lighting, is being built purely for the benefit of fish. In a restricted area which underwater hunters are not allowed to enter, various hollow structures of metal, concrete, and plastic are being erected on the sea bed. Skin-diving biologists will examine them from time to time to discover which style of architecture the fish prefer. Artificial lights will be switched on, and chemicals pumped into various quarters of the town through pipelines, to study the reactions of the fish. The aim of this novel experiment is to find the conditions which allow fish to grow most rapidly, and any discoveries resulting from it will be of practical value to fishermen all over the world.

In a less scientific way, attempts are also being made in the United States to improve the housing conditions of fish. Artificial reefs have been constructed for their benefit by the delightfully simple method of dumping old automobile bodies into the sea. This serves two very useful purposes — it gets rid of the old cars, and gives shelter to fish which otherwise could never survive on open, sandy sea beds where they would have nowhere to hide from their enemies.

Now all this is very important, and may decide how well

the human race is fed ten or twenty years from now — but no one can pretend that it is very exciting or romantic. Farming seldom is, either on land or sea, except in times of natural disasters. And at least the farmers of the sea will be spared the chief catastrophes which menace their comrades on land — floods and droughts.

There is, however, one possible way of exploiting the creatures of the sea that is as thrilling and dramatic as anything that has ever been done in the past. This is the protection, breeding, and herding of the mightiest animals in the world — the whales.

Just now we mentioned the Indians and the bison they once chased over the great plains. As far as the whales are concerned, we are still "buffalo hunters." If we want to be up to date, it's time we started cattle ranching.

For whales are cattle, even though they weigh a hundred tons or more. This fact has long been recognized in the use of the terms bull, cow and calf in connection with them. As we have already pointed out, they are intelligent creatures who can communicate with each other by means of under-water sounds, so it should not be difficult to direct and control them, perhaps with additional help from electric fields. Most of them are docile — even playful — except when attacked. Then some have been known to hit back and even to sink small ships by ramming them.

Today, some fifty thousand of these great animals are killed every year, providing much valuable oil, meat, and other food products. You may never have eaten whale meat, but when properly prepared, it tastes very much like beef. The Japanese regard it as a great delicacy, and one day other nations will do the same — more familiar kinds of meat will be getting steadily scarcer and more expensive.

It is important to realize that there are two entirely

different types of whales. The largest and most numerous are the "baleen" or "whalebone" whales, which get their name from the hanging curtains of whalebone (baleen) which fringe their mouths in place of teeth. They live almost exclusively on a diet of small shrimplike creatures which abound in countless billions in the cold arctic and antarctic waters, where — as explained in Chapter 6 — the sea's crop of plankton is the richest. Straining this living soup through their built-in filters, the baleen whales have no need of teeth, and despite their huge size their throats are only about six inches in diameter. So none of them could have swallowed Jonah.

Very different, indeed, is the sperm whale — the original Moby Dick of Herman Melville's great novel. He does not feed on two-inch shrimps, but upon one of the most terrible creatures of the sea. Diving to depths of half a mile or more, the sperm whale hunts the giant squids in the eternal darkness where they live, chewing them up alive despite their efforts to defend themselves with claw-studded tentacles and vicious parrot beaks. Although most of the squid eaten are relatively small — less than six feet in length — fragments of single tentacles thirty feet long have been found in the stomachs of sperm whales. We'll return to these giant and mysterious creatures in chapter ten.

The sperm whales live mostly in the warm seas around the equator, but the baleen whales migrate every year in one of the greatest animal movements on the face of the earth. They spend the summers in the polar regions, feasting on the rich crop of plankton life that flourishes as the sun rises higher in the sky. At the end of the summer, gorged with tons of food they have consumed, they move toward the equator so that their calves can be born in warm waters.

The largest of the baleen whales — the blue or sulphur-bottom whale — is the biggest animal that has ever existed. Not even the dinosaurs of prehistoric times approached it in size. It grows to a length of well over a hundred feet, and although only a few have ever been weighed carefully, the biggest specimens must tip the scales at something like 200 tons. (The heaviest actually weighed came to over 150 tons; it was 89 feet long, and lengths of 110 feet have been recorded. So my guess of 200 tons for the real giants may even be a little on the small side.)

A baby blue whale is about twenty-three feet long when born and weighs approximately eight tons. It's rather hard to picture a baby as big as a bus, and it's even harder to grasp the rate at which it grows. Feeding only on its mother's milk, the infant takes a mere seven or eight months to become a forty or fifty tonner. Whale milk is extremely rich in fats — much more so than cow's milk — and to enable her baby to grow at such a speed the mother must produce something like a ton of milk a day. This is a thought that should make a dairy farmer's eyes pop.

It was once believed that whales live to enormous ages — perhaps hundreds of years — and take correspondingly long to become mature. But it is just the opposite. A whale is full grown at two, can be a parent at three, and has reached a ripe old age at fifty.

All the facts and figures about whales are a little overwhelming, but here is one more that is very important to our present argument. The value of the meat and oil products in a single large whale can be as much as thirty thousand dollars. No wonder that many nations send fleets of factory ships and catchers into the antarctic each summer to hunt these floating gold mines. And no wonder that they were threatened with total extinction before international regulations limited the annual catch.

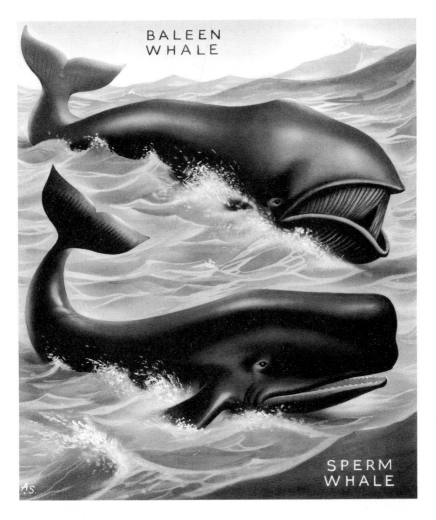

BALEEN
WHALE

SPERM
WHALE

When you consider how farmers have improved the standard of all domestic animals by breeding them for desired qualities, it is obvious that whales provide us with wonderful opportunities in this direction. With our modern resources, we should have no great difficulty in taming, or at least controlling, whales. The first men to tame elephants, more than two thousand years ago, faced a much more formidable challenge.

Granted that it is possible to herd and breed whales as we do the more familiar, and much tinier, cattle of the land, what would be the advantages? Well, we could steer them to new feeding grounds where they could feast on artificially fertilized crops, and grow more rapidly than they do under natural conditions. We could protect them from their natural enemies, the swift and ravenous killer whales. We might even, as I have already suggested, train those fierce monsters to act as marine sheep dogs, herding our flocks for us. We could improve the amount and quality of the food products they yield and could eliminate today's cruel and wasteful methods of slaughtering.

It might also be possible to keep herds of milch whales, purely for the ton or so of milk they produce every day. Designing a milking machine for a whale would be an interesting engineering problem, but not a very difficult one, for the whale does all the work. When her calf wishes to feed, which must be fairly often — it puts on weight at the rate of about five hundred pounds a day — the mother whale literally squirts her milk into the baby's mouth in a high-speed, powerful jet. This forced-feeding technique has presumably evolved so that whale calves can suckle while submerged, without getting sea water into their mouths.

Whale milk, incidentally, is much too rich for direct human consumption, although one could probably acquire a taste for it. But it would be an extremely valuable source of fats and other foods, once it had been properly processed.

Some people may doubt whether it would be possible to get such enormous and powerful animals to obey our instructions and to do exactly what we wanted. However, the work already carried out in training porpoises shows how intelligent and cooperative the marine mammals can be. Both whales and porpoises belong to the same order of the animal kingdom — the cetacean. In any event, it may soon be possible to control even the most untameable creatures by passing weak electric currents into the proper areas of their brains. This has been done experimentally with monkeys without causing any harm or distress to the animal. So we may develop some kind of radio control unit for whales, permanently installed on the leaders of the herds, which would be switched on when we wished them to carry out our orders.

In a novel called *The Deep Range* I tried to describe how "whale ranchers" some fifty years from now would use midget submarines to control and protect their great beasts. The parallel with the old-time cowboy is obvious, but it cannot be taken too far. The ranches of the sea will be thousands of miles across. Indeed, their borders will not be fixed, for they will move from the polar regions to the equator with the seasons. They may well be too large and too costly for single countries to run, and will probably be managed by some billion-dollar international organization. Such old-fashioned ideas as whale rustling, or shooting it out with the boys from the rival ranch, hardly fit into this picture. Maybe that is a pity — but the life of a twenty-first century whale-boy will still have plenty of excitement, even though he may use an atomic-powered submarine instead of a horse, and curtains of electric impulses in place of a lariat.

Perhaps this is an amusing dream that will never come true. Many things which are technically possible fail to happen because something else comes along that makes them unnecessary by doing the same job in a different way. To give an example from the recent past, not so long ago most people believed that the future of aviation belonged to the airship, which in the 1930's carried fare-paying passengers across the Atlantic in a comfort and quietness not

achieved by the airplane until twenty years later. The
prophets of that time were sure that, before long, great fleets
of Zeppelins would be flying between all the capitals of the
world.

It might easily have happened, but a series of disasters
put an end to the giant gas bags, and commercial lighter-
than-air flying machines went the way of the dinosaurs. So
although we have power and speed, our age has missed the
most impressive, and some say most beautiful, of all the
ships that have ever moved through the sky.

In the same way, no one may ever run a whale ranch
because we may find more efficient — if less romantic —
methods of getting food from the sea. And this brings us
right back to the basic principles of food production in the
ocean which we've already touched upon in chapter six.

Remember how everything in the sea feeds on some
smaller and simpler living creature, right down to the microscopic plankton plants which alone can combine the raw
materials in the water into the chemicals of life. As a result
we have a food chain which may run like this —

man
> *feeds on fish which*
>> *feed on smaller fish which*
>>> *feed on plankton animals which*
>>>> *feed on plankton plants which*
>>>>> *"feed" on salts and chemicals in the sea*

You'll notice that I've put the last "feed" in quotation
marks because we don't normally consider plants as feeding.
It is more accurate to picture them as tiny chemical factories,
which take in simple raw materials such as water, carbon
dioxide, phosphates, nitrates — and of course sunlight —

and build them up into the much more complicated substances which animals must consume for nourishment. So
plants could get along quite well (maybe better) without
animals — and did so when the earth was young. But every
land or sea animal in the world depends ultimately upon
plants for its source of food.

All this we've already discussed, but now there is a new
aspect of the food chain I want to point out. Nothing in the
world is a hundred per cent efficient, and each link in this
chain of life involves a considerable loss of energy and
material. For example, when a fish eats a pound of plankton,
it doesn't gain a pound in weight. It may not even gain
anything at all, for it may have used all the energy it gets
from its food in the sheer effort of finding it! And, of course,
all food contains some material — often a good deal — which
is not nourishing, and so has to be discarded without profit
to the animal eating it.

When they are all added up, the losses in each link of the
food chain are surprisingly high. In fact, a man has to eat
about ten pounds of fish to get one pound of nourishment;
a fish has to eat ten pounds of animal plankton to build up
its weight by one pound, and the plankton animals need the
same ten-to-one ratio of plankton plants to feed them. Of
course, this is a very rough estimate, but is close enough to
show the laws that are involved in the chain of life.

Consider what these numbers imply. They mean that to
gain just one pound of nourishment a man has to eat:

10 pounds of fish
which eat
100 pounds of plankton animals
which eat
1000 pounds of plankton plants

The sea, therefore, must produce a thousand pounds, or *half a ton* of living matter for us to gain a *single pound* out of it. Doesn't this seem an appalling waste? Perhaps you'll appreciate it better if these amounts are shown pictorially, as in the diagram below.

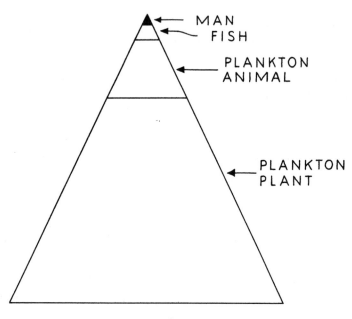

FIGURE 1.

This is called the food pyramid. The area below each level shows the total amount of food that must be produced to maintain the levels above it, and you'll see at a glance how tiny is the fraction we use. Sometimes there are even more levels than those shown here, each involving the same ten-to-one loss. For example, if we eat a fish that has eaten other fish (as most of them do) instead of browsing on plankton animals directly, we get an extra level in the food pyramid and the figures may build up to these staggering totals —

To gain

1 pound, a man
eats
10 pounds of tuna
which eat
100 pounds of sardines
which eat
1000 pounds of plankton animals
which eat
10,000 pounds of plankton plants

So in this case the sea must provide altogether some five tons of living material for us to profit by one pound! You can hardly see our share of the sea's total production in this case, as shown pictorially in Figure 2.

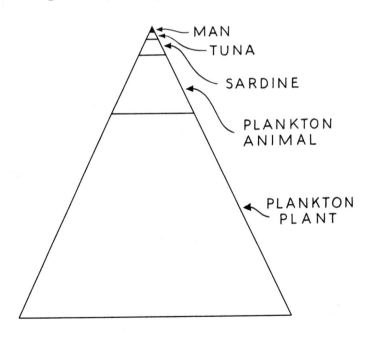

FIGURE 2.

Too bad, you may say — but what can we do about it? Well, we could use far more of the food produced in the sea if we bypassed some of these stages. To show what I mean, let's take an example which is a little farfetched, but which brings the problem clearly into focus.

Suppose the food pyramid shown in Figure 2 was the only one that existed, and we had to support ourselves on that. In actual fact, of course, there are hundreds of pyramids, including shorter and more important ones like man-cow-grass or man-chicken-grain. Imagine, if you can, that the entire human race lived on tuna — a monotonous prospect, I know, but this is merely for the sake of demonstration.

Now it is simple arithmetic that, if we could exterminate all the tuna and catch instead all the sardines which *they* would have eaten, we'd have ten times as much food — and ten times as many people could live on the earth. Taking the argument still further, if we could exterminate the sardines as well and could catch all the plankton animals *they'd* have eaten, then there would be enough food for a hundred times as many people — assuming, of course, that men could eat plankton animals, a point I'll come to in a moment. And even the next and final step is possible in theory — if we could kill *all* the animals in the sea and eat the plankton plants — why, a thousand men could live for every one who had dined on tuna!

You may amuse yourself by trying to shoot holes in this argument. It isn't difficult, of course. But the first objection which may occur to you is not as valid as you may think. If you say "I *like* tuna and I'm darned if I'll eat sardines," consider this point: If you did live in a world that was so short of food that such a choice had to be made, would you insist on eating tuna if you knew this meant death by star-

vation to ten men who were willing to live on sardines, or
to a hundred men who would eat plankton animals, or to a
thousand who would eat plankton plants?

Luckily, the choice would never be as brutally simple and
straightforward as this, but the example does make clear this
vitally important fact — the lower down the food pyramid
we can draw our nourishment, the more mouths we can feed,
and the less will be the danger of starvation on this earth.
Some foods are luxuries which we may not be able to afford
because they involve the wastage of far greater quantities
of other foods.

"Shorten the food chain!" should be the battle cry of the
future. It may not have the appeal of "Give me liberty or
give me death!" or "My country, right or wrong!" but the
time has passed for slogans which stirred only the blood and
not the brain. The enemy we have to fight now is nature,
not our fellow men.

Now, there are some food chains which simply cannot be
shortened. Perhaps the best example is the man-cow-grass
one. It takes ten pounds of grass to make a pound of cow,
but it wouldn't help us to kill all the cows in the world,
because we can't eat grass.

However, some of the food chains in the sea could be
drastically shortened, at least in theory, if we concentrated
on suitable products. During the last few years there has
been much talk about harvesting plankton for human (or
farm animal) consumption, and some experiments have been
carried out to see if this is possible. There is no doubt that
plankton can be used as a basis for foods — in fact, it is
extremely nourishing — but the great problem is collecting
it. The plankton plants and animals are so small that it is
not easy to strain them out of the water on a large enough

scale to make it worth while. Only in areas that are exceptionally rich in plankton — where the sea is almost a soup,
in fact — would collection be practical.

One day, therefore, we may set up plankton farms in the
most fertile areas of the sea, and harvest the crop with mile-
long skimmers moving across the surface — the combine
harvesters of the ocean plains. Or we may pump the water
through vast filters, extracting the food we need just as the
whales do. One can imagine a ship that was really a
mechanical whale, with filtering gear at the bows, which
would steam through the plankton fields scooping up the
crop as it went.

Whatever techniques we use, plankton farming will not be
cheap or easy. In fact, it may turn out that it is more eco-
nomical to let a marine animal do the job for us, and then
to catch the animal. Of course, it's essential to choose the
most efficient animal — otherwise we're right back where
we started with our present-day methods of fishing.

The animal that shows the biggest promise as a plankton
collector which men could also eat, is one we have already
mentioned — the small shrimplike creatures known scien-
tifically as Euphausiidae, and called krill or whale food by
the whalers because they are the main food of the baleen
whales. It has been estimated that the largest whales consume about three tons of krill a day, and that the total production in the antarctic every year is not less than a billion
tons.

One of the things that makes krill attractive as a food
source is that these animals feed directly on the plankton
plants — not on other animals. So we have shortened the
food chain to the utmost, and can get ten times as much
food if we catch krill directly than if we hunt the whales that
eat the krill. One scientist who has studied the problem

believes that even now it might be more profitable to scoop up krill than to go hunting whales. It would certainly be much easier, as the little creatures swarm in thickly packed shoals covering enormous areas of the sea.

At this point, if not before, you may well wonder what some of these new foods will taste like. Scientists who have eaten small plankton animals like krill report that they are delicious, and regard them as a luxury. The recipe given by one is, "Boil in sea water for a moment, strain and fry in butter, then serve on toast." Other plankton pastes are considerably less attractive, and would probably be used only as meal for poultry and other livestock. But the important fact is that these floating pastures of the sea can provide an almost limitless source of the raw materials — the proteins, fats, carbohydrates and vitamins — which the foodstuffs industry needs. We can trust the chemists of the future to make the final result tasty to the consumer. Already, without realizing it, we eat a wide variety of marine products in our ordinary foods. Did you know that seaweed goes into almost all jellies, jams and ice creams? It is quite possible that the majority of the foods displayed in a supermarket twenty or thirty years from now will bear names completely unfamiliar to us today, and will have come directly or indirectly from the sea.

Looking even further ahead, we can imagine the day when farming, for all practical purposes, will have abandoned the continents and moved out into the ocean. Why should we struggle to raise crops on the dry desert, which even the most fertile soil appears to be when compared with the sea? The time may come when only a few luxury products — fruits, for example — will be grown on land, and all else will come from the ocean.

It is hard for us to picture such a state of affairs. We tend to assume that farms of the type we know have always existed, and that there is no other way to raise food. But farms are quite recent inventions in the million-year story of mankind, and nothing lasts forever.

The rice fields of China and India, the grain covered prairies of the American Midwest — these will not be enough to nourish the billions of the future. And so to our great-grandchildren the word "farm" may have a totally different meaning than to us. It will make them think, not of wheat fields waving in the sun or of cattle moving across the plains, but of vast, floating factories skimming up the richest of all harvests, far to the south amid the crystal glitter of antarctic ice.

chapter 9

Wealth from the Waves

THE sea contains much more than water. This fact is obvious, of course, whenever you accidentally swallow a mouthful of it. One of the very first scientific discoveries of primitive man must have been that the sea is salt, and does not provide a refreshing drink like the water of lakes and rivers. It is only during the last century, however, that we have learned what a multitude of substances salt includes.

A list of all the materials in the sea would fill a book as large as a telephone directory. In fact, there is probably a little of everything in the sea. The great rivers of the world drain into it from all the continents, carrying out into the oceans untold billions of tons of minerals from the land. Some of this burden dissolves in the sea, and some falls to the bottom. The net result is that over the ages the sea has slowly gathered at least a trace of all the chemicals that exist in the world. It is still gathering them. The seas of the far future will be saltier than those of today, and ours are saltier than those of a billion years ago.

If you were to take a hundred pounds of sea water and heat it in a pan, when all the water had boiled off you would be left with about three pounds of dirty white crystals. A little more than two pounds of this would be common salt — sodium chloride — and the remaining pound would be a very complicated mixture containing almost every element you care to mention — even such rare substances as gold and radium. Of course, these would be present only in the most minute traces, but there is so much water in the oceans that even a trace of any element adds up to a tremendous quantity in the sea as a whole.

Here are some figures which may give you an idea of the amount of material in the sea. We won't consider the entire sea, but just a small portion of it. A mile is a distance easy enough to picture — after all, you can walk it in ten or fifteen minutes. So try to imagine a cube of sea water a mile on each side — one cubic mile, in other words. It doesn't seem such an enormous amount of water, so let's see what it contains.

First, we must find out how much that single cubic mile of water weighs. You might like to guess the figure. A thousand tons? A million? Nowhere near. The right answer is something like four *billion* tons!

If you could boil all that water away, which would be quite an operation, you would be left with a hill of salt weighing about 150 million tons. Some 120 million tons of this would be common table salt, and most of the rest compounds of magnesium, calcium and potassium. There would, for example, be about 8 million tons of magnesium sulphate — better known as Epsom salts; enough to give a five-pound supply to every man, woman and child on earth.

Most of the metals would be there, combined with other elements, in amounts ranging from sixty thousand tons for strontium down to a fraction of an ounce for radium. Near the bottom of the list, but still in appreciable amounts, would be the precious metals, gold and silver. Although the estimates vary a great deal, according to some experts our cubic mile of sea water might contain as much as twenty-five tons of gold, and forty-five tons of silver.

When you consider that we have been discussing the

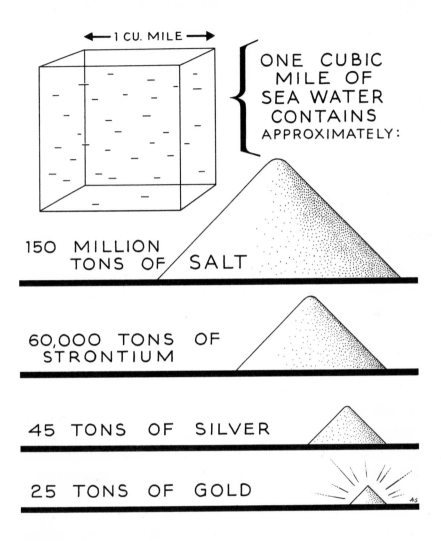

ONE CUBIC MILE OF SEA WATER CONTAINS APPROXIMATELY:

150 MILLION TONS OF SALT

60,000 TONS OF STRONTIUM

45 TONS OF SILVER

25 TONS OF GOLD

contents of a single cubic mile, and there are over 300 million such cubes in the sea as a whole, then it is obvious that the mineral wealth of the oceans is beyond all imagination. Can you picture eight billion tons of gold? This is what the sea holds, according to some estimates. And more useful metals, such as nickel, copper, uranium, lead, zinc and manganese, are present in vastly greater quantities.

In view of this fact, you may wonder why anyone bothers to mine the land, especially since digging up and crushing rocks is so much more difficult than pumping water. Unfortunately, sea mining, even though there are unlimited amounts of the raw material lapping against every coast line, is not so easy as it looks. The great difficulty is that such huge quantities of water have to be processed to obtain the wanted materials that it doesn't pay, except for a very few substances.

One of these is the element bromine, an essential ingredient in modern gasolines and photographic materials. Antiknock gasolines contain a chemical called ethylene dibromide — hence the name ethyl — and when they were introduced in the 1920's they increased enormously the demand for bromine. There was just not enough bromine on the land, so the chemists had to get it from the sea, where, luckily, it is one of the commoner substances.

A cubic mile of sea water contains over a quarter of a million tons of bromine — nothing like that 120 million tons of table salt, but still a sizable amount. The Dow Chemical Company set to work to extract it, and built the first large-scale plant to do this on the North Carolina coast in 1933. The process used is a fairly simple one, depending on a principle very familiar in everyday life. Bromine has a close chemical relative, the element chlorine, which is much more active and energetic. When chlorine is bubbled through sea water it dislodges the bromine from its compounds like two relatives who can't stand each other — one moves out when the other moves in.

The Dow bromine process was an historic milestone in chemical engineering, for it was the first time anyone had extracted an element directly from sea water on the commercial scale. It was followed a few years later by an equally important achievement — the production of the light metal magnesium from the sea.

Magnesium is used in very large quantities in the aircraft industry — a large airplane may contain a ton of it. During the war there was naturally a tremendous demand for the metal, and, as there are about five million tons of it in every cubic mile of sea water, there are inexhaustible supplies washing against every coast. Once again the Dow Company met the challenge, and today practically the entire United States production of magnesium is from the ocean. Tens of thousands of tons of metal come out of the waves every year — truly a modern miracle.

Our success in extracting bromine and magnesium from sea water has naturally made men wonder if other elements can be obtained from the same source. Unfortunately, the metals we would like to mine — such as copper and lead — are present only in very small proportions, and enormous quantities of water would have to be processed to get at them. It was difficult enough to extract magnesium from the sea — but copper is almost a million times scarcer.

There have been attempts to win gold from the sea, but they have all been commercial failures, for the cost of extraction far outweighed the value of the metal. After the first world war, the great German chemist, Fritz Haber, hoped to pay off his country's war debts in this way — although it should have been obvious that if a really successful method of obtaining gold from sea water were discovered, the metal would no longer be worth much. A research ship, the *Meteor*, was fitted out for the quest and explored the Atlantic for three years between 1924 and 1928. It found very little gold, but brought back vast scientific information, which in the long run was probably more valuable.

One enterprising Australian actually set up a small ocean gold-mining plant in 1935 and processed some fifty tons of water a day. He did succeed in extracting a few ounces of the metal, but it was probably the most expensive gold ever mined, and the operation soon closed down.

So, despite the immense quantities of rare metals in the sea, the problem of recovery seems hopeless. The old expression "like looking for a needle in a haystack" fits the case of gold rather well. If you take a volume of sea water the size of the average haystack, the amount of gold in it would just about make a small needle.

However, there have been many things in the past which once seemed impossible because of engineering difficulties, but which are now taken for granted. Some of the problems which had to be overcome before atomic energy could be released were greater than those involved in extracting metals from sea water, and as the mines on land become exhausted we may be forced to turn to the oceans.

Some of the creatures in the sea have set us an example by showing that they can do better than our chemists. The metal, cobalt, is even scarcer than gold in the sea, yet some lobsters manage to extract it, while the humble oyster concentrates the stray particles of copper from the gallons of water it flushes through its gills. These achievements suggest that we may be able to select marine plants or animals which can do our mining for us. Indeed, in at least one case we have already done this. The element iodine — another member of the bromine-chlorine family — is present in sea water only in a few parts in a hundred million, but seaweeds manage to extract it from their food, and until recently all our supplies of this substance came from seaweed ashes. Can we encourage marine plants to look for other elements? There is certainly a vast field of research here for the biochemist.

When he discovers how these simple creatures perform such complicated chemical operations, our fears of metal shortages may be ended forever.

When we do begin large-scale sea-mining operations, it will be important to choose the right place to work. One of the best sites would be the Dead Sea, where for millions of years the hot sun has been evaporating the water so that the concentration of salts has built up until it is five times as great as in the open ocean. The Dead Sea, therefore, is one of the richest chemical treasure-troves in the world, still almost untouched. If the Israeli scientists (who are working hard on the problem) find a way of tapping its wealth on the large scale, this may change the entire way of life of their country and, indeed, of the whole Middle East. We live in an age when the patterns of politics are created by scientists, not by statesmen.

Another place to look for great mineral resources will be the bed of the ocean. Most of the heavier metals, which are not actually dissolved in the sea, but float in it as a dust of finely divided particles, may by now have settled to the bottom. The sludge lying on the sea bed may be far richer than the waters above it. One day we may pump it up to the surface and use it as the raw material for our factories.

Something of this sort has been suggested quite recently in connection with another untouched marine resource. As long ago as 1875, the scientists of the British *Challenger* expedition — the first deep-sea expedition, which set the pattern for most of those to come — made a puzzling discovery. They found that large areas of the sea bed were covered with potato-shaped lumps of manganese dioxide, up to a foot across. Manganese — not to be confused with the magnesium we've already mentioned — is very important in metallurgy for it is used in making steels and other alloys.

These nodules lying on the ocean floor also contain considerable amounts of the much more valuable metals, nickel and cobalt, and are built up in layers rather like onions. At their centers they usually have small hard cores, such as pieces of volcanic glass, sharks' teeth, or the earbones of whales. For some reason, these have acted as seeds around which the nodules have grown layer by layer, taking millions of years to reach their present size.

But the origin of these manganese nodules, although of great scientific interest, is perhaps less important than their enormous extent. Millions of square miles of the Atlantic and Pacific floors are carpeted with them, just lying on the sea bed waiting to be picked up. The total amount of metal involved is far more than the human race has mined since the beginning of history. Some estimates put the figure as high as two hundred billion tons.

The difficulty, of course, is that this bonanza is two or three miles below the surface of the sea. How are we going to get it up?

John L. Mero, an engineer at the University of California's Institute of Marine Resources, has made a detailed study of the problem. There are two ways of lifting material from the deep sea, but none that has even been used to collect the very large amounts — thousands of tons a day — that would be needed for commercial mining operations.

One method is to use a dredge, like the bucket of a mechanical excavator, and to lower it on a chain to the sea bed. When it is pulled along the bottom, it will scoop up several tons of nodules which can then be hauled to the surface. But this is a slow business, for it would take the dredge several minutes to make the trip each way.

A better idea is to use hydraulic power — that is, to suck

up the nodules in a kind of submarine vacuum cleaner. The operation could then be carried out continuously, but the engineering problems involved in pumping thousands of tons of material up a pipe several miles high — looking at it from the point of view of the sea bed — are very great. Perhaps someone will come up with a new and unexpected solution, as has happened so often in the past. It will be worth the effort, for in some areas of the Pacific there is more than a million dollars of mineral wealth lying on every square mile.

One day — perhaps in the very near future — this untouched treasure will give the international lawyers one of their biggest headaches. For whom does it belong to? Can anyone with the necessary equipment go and pick it up?

Like the ownership of outer space, the question of property rights on the sea bed has never been of practical importance until today. It is something that will have to be settled before long, especially if any valuable underwater strikes are made. Perhaps the great gold rushes of a century ago may be repeated on the sea bed, with submarine prospectors staking out their claims. But those prospectors will not be grizzled old-timers working alone. They will be multimillion dollar corporations employing armies of scientists and technicians.

In some areas, of course, the exploitation of the sea bed has already begun. Offshore oil wells are now drilling for petroleum many miles out at sea in the Gulf of Mexico and off the coast of California. At first, the drilling was done from great platforms standing on piles driven deep into the ocean floor, but recently a daring new technique has been worked out in which the entire operation is performed from an anchored ship. All the drilling equipment is lowered to the sea bed, where it digs itself in by remote control. Through underwater TV cameras, the operators can watch

what is happening and the drilling can be carried out exactly as on land, despite the fact that the wellsite may be a thousand feet down — much too deep for divers to reach.

This new technique of underwater drilling may soon make possible one of the most fascinating of all the experiments which scientists are planning in the sea. This is the sinking of a shaft right through the crust of the earth — a project we will discuss in chapter eleven.

In the long run, the most valuable substance in the sea is not gold or manganese or bromine. It is something we normally take for granted — water. Many a shipwrecked sailor, dying of thirst, as hundreds do every year, even now, would trade all the mineral wealth of the seas for a glass of water.

The sea is the great reservoir, the original source of all the rain that falls from the skies, even in areas thousands of miles from the nearest ocean. Like a huge boiler warmed by the sun, the sea gives up millions of tons of water vapor which is carried around the world by the winds, and eventually forms the clouds which shower it back to earth.

In many lands there is far too little rain. Indeed, there are some countries where it is almost unknown. Great areas of the world which were once fertile plains and farms are now desert because the streams and wells which once watered them dried up centuries ago. Yet all around us, in the ocean, is enough water to drown the continents miles deep.

It is easy to get fresh water out of sea water. Boiling it is the simplest way, so that pure water comes off as vapor which can be condensed, while the salts remain as brine. This is the way of the sun and the winds, and it is the way that ships at sea obtain their water. But it is fairly expensive and requires distilling equipment and the heat to run it. Water prepared by this method costs many times as much

as most people are prepared to pay for it, except on islands
or places like the Arabian oil fields where drinking water
may be more expensive than gasoline. Nevertheless, a great
deal of ingenuity and scientific skill have gone into designing
distillation plants to obtain fresh water from the sea, and
million-gallon-a-day units are now being built by the United
States Department of the Interior's Office of Saline Water.

Distilled water from the sea may be another of the many
by-products of atomic energy, for here is a limitless source
of heat to run the stills. In chapter six we suggested a way
in which atomic power might be used to fertilize the deserts
of the sea. Perhaps one day it may also bring life to the
deserts of the land.

Boiling is rather a brute-force way of getting fresh water
from the sea. There may be neater answers. One of them
is suggested by this question, which has probably not occurred to one person in a hundred. How do fish drink? And
not only fish, but other animals that spend all their lives in
the ocean, such as whales and sea birds? Do they have
built-in salt water conversion plants?

As a matter of fact, they do. There are certain thin films
or membranes which can filter the salts out of sea water,
and marine animals have these in the cells of their bodies.
You may be familiar with something of the sort in your own
home if you live in a region which has hard water — that is,
water containing an unusually high proportion of lime.
Water softeners, which contain porous filters, can remove
the unwanted chemicals so that only the pure, sweet liquid
passes through.

Since the war, partly as a result of the atomic energy pro-
gram — which has sparked scientific discoveries in hundreds
of different fields — types of filters have been prepared which
can perform the most remarkable feats. Not only can some

of them strain almost all of the salt out of sea water, but others can act selectively — that is to say, they can trap one chemical from a solution and let the rest go through. They act, in other words, almost like sieves.

And this brings us right back to the problem of extracting rare metals from sea water. One day, perhaps, we may be able to develop these chemical sieves to such a degree of perfection that we can extract any substance we need from the sea — and do it economically. Water will flow inland down a canal or pipeline, and at various points along it, the raw materials of civilization will be tapped off — the common salt, the magnesium, the bromine, the copper, — yes, even the gold. And at the end of the line, spreading out into a great lake which may be used to irrigate a continent, will be the most precious product of all — pure, crystal water.

chapter 10

Monsters of the Night

WHEN I was a boy I came across a
picture that has haunted me all my life. It was an illustra-
tion in a book about whaling called *The Cruise of the
Cachalot* by Frank Bullen, and it showed two incredible
sea monsters locked together in a death struggle. One was
the great sperm whale — itself a weird enough beast with
its square box of a head and the narrow jaw hinged like a
saw underneath it. But the thing it was fighting might have
come straight from a nightmare. It was a huge, flabby mass
sprouting a forest of sucker-studded arms which had wrapped
themselves around the head and jaw of the whale. From the
midst of this tangle of tentacles, two immense eyes, as big
as dinner plates, stared out with a cold and evil intelligence.
It was the most terrifying thing I had ever seen, and I could
hardly believe that it was real.

It was many years before I knew that the artist had not
exaggerated, and that the giant squid he had drawn actually
existed, just as he had shown it. This was my first introduction to the mystery of the sea, and it taught me that there
are creatures in the ocean of a size and strangeness that no
one could ever imagine.

There can be very little doubt that there are other sea
monsters, perhaps even stranger and larger, still completely
unknown to us. The sea has given us many surprises in the
past, and may give us many more in the future.

For years, the Great Sea Serpent has been a figure of fun,

and those who claimed to have seen it were regarded as hoaxes, crackpots, or drunks. Times have changed, and today many scientists take the sea serpent very seriously indeed although, as we'll see later, they are pretty sure it is *not* a serpent. There are several reasons for this new attitude. Perhaps the most important is something that happened in South Africa during the Christmas week of 1938.

The story of the coelacanth has often been told before, but is worth repeating because it is one of the most extraordinary discoveries of our times, and a fine lesson to anyone foolish enough to imagine that the sea has no more secrets. The coelacanth (pronounced seal-a-kanth) is a species of fish well known to students of fossils, as it flourished about forty million years ago when the great reptiles ruled the earth. It was thought to have died out with them, until the scientific world was electrified by the news that one had been caught in a net, very much alive. If a dinosaur had been discovered in some Amazon swamp, it would scarcely have been a greater surprise to the zoologists — for the terrible lizards still trampled the earth millions of years after the last coelacanth was believed to have died.

Fourteen years passed before the second of these living fossils was found in a remote group of islands between Madagascar and East Africa. The first was apparently a stray, two thousand miles from home, which was one reason why it took so long to find another. The story of the hunt has been brilliantly told by the man largely responsible for its success, Professor J. L. B. Smith, in his book *The Search Beneath the Sea,* and is far more exciting than any detective story.

Since 1952, half a dozen more of these remarkable fish have been caught, and we now know that, far from being extinct, they are not even particularly rare. The reason why

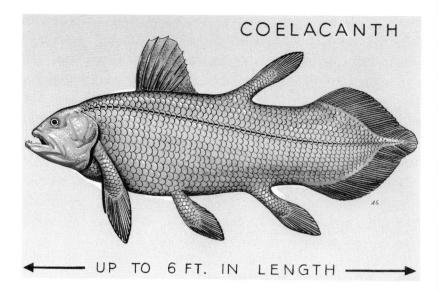

COELACANTH

UP TO 6 FT. IN LENGTH

science had never come across them before is that they live in an out-of-the-way place, and are hard to catch.

Although the coelacanth is a large fish — growing to at least six feet in length — it is certainly no monster, and one might argue that its discovery proves nothing about the possibility of very large, unknown animals in the sea. However, we must realize that it would be extremely difficult to learn anything about such creatures if they spent all their lives in the deep sea. They would be far below the level at which fishermen operate, and even if caught by nets or hooks would probably break away. The very few bathyscape and bathysphere descents would have taught us nothing about them, for the brilliant lights would have scared them off. After all, how much could explorers from outer space learn of the animals on the surface of this earth if they had to hunt for them by lowering grabs or nets or observation chambers? They would not catch one animal in a thousand. Only slow-moving creatures like snails and tortoises would ever be captured — all the rest could easily escape.

About the only time we can hope to discover large and shy deep-sea animals is when they die and float to the surface, or are cast ashore by storms. But this must be very unusual. In the sea, most dead animals are torn to pieces long before they can reach any coast line. Think of all the fish in the ocean — and how rarely you see a dead one on the beach! Even when this rare event did happen, the chances are ten to one that the animal concerned would be cast ashore on some remote beach where no one would ever see it, and in such a damaged condition that it would be unrecognizable. Even well-known creatures like whales and sharks, which are sometimes washed ashore, are often so decayed that only experts can identify them, and before a qualified zoologist arrives on the spot the remains give rise to all sorts of false rumors about unknown sea monsters.

The case of the giant squid provides a very good example of this. For centuries, there have been stories of a terrible, many-armed sea monster called the kraken, which attacked ships and dragged them down into the water. Indeed, such tales go back to the time of Homer, three thousand years ago. You may remember how Ulysses had to steer his ship between the whirlpool, Charybdis, and the tentacled monster, Scylla, who snatched one of his sailors as a toll charge.

The people of the Middle Ages enjoyed hearing such tales and believed them completely. But with the rise of modern science, they were all dismissed as myths — probably tall stories told by sailors who, just as they do today, amused themselves by pulling landsmen's legs.

About a hundred years ago, however, it was discovered that the legend of the kraken is founded on fact, even though its size had been greatly exaggerated. The New England whalemen must have been among the first to see and actually handle the giant squid — although it was already dead and usually in small pieces when they did so. The daring hunters of the sperm whale noticed that the heads of these great animals are usually marked with scars in the form of circular sucker marks. These were evidence of mighty battles in the depths of the sea, and in the stomachs of the whales they found the cause of the scars — claw-studded tentacles as thick as a man's arm, sometimes up to thirty feet in length.

Since then, giant squids have been cast ashore from time to time on the coasts of Newfoundland and the British Isles, and naturalists have been able to examine them. They are truly terrifying creatures, and no one knows how large they can grow. The biggest specimen actually measured was about fifty-five feet in length; twenty feet of this was the body, and the remaining thirty-five feet included two very long, thin tentacles which the animal probably used as feelers. Its eight main tentacles are less than half of the length of the two big ones, so a fifty-five-foot squid is not really quite as big as it sounds. The main bulk, when you neglect the feelers, is about forty feet long.

But there is no reason to suppose that this is anywhere near the limit of size, and it would be strange indeed if the world's biggest squid had been among the very few cast ashore to be examined and measured by naturalists. There may well be specimens more than a hundred feet in length. In fact, we have some indirect evidence that this is the case.

The suckers of that fifty-five-foot squid were about four inches across. However, it has been reported — how reliably I do not know — that whales have been found bearing the scars of suckers eighteen inches in diameter. This implies, if we do some simple arithmetic, a squid two hundred and fifty feet long. We can be quite (well, almost) sure that such a size is impossible. But the thought of a sucker eighteen inches across is enough to make anyone's hair stand on end.

In the case of the giant squid, therefore, we have a very large animal which has never been seen alive except in a few rare instances when it came to the surface and was probably dying. We know nothing of its habits and have never been able to catch one — it would be quite a handful if we did. Yet it is not rare. On the contrary, it seems to be very common, half a mile down in the sea.

Many deep-sea animals, perhaps including the giant squid, avoid the light and may even be injured by it, so if they come to the surface at all it is only during the night. This, of course, makes them even less likely to be seen by man, especially from the decks of a modern ship thrashing its noisy way along, its engines scaring everything within miles.

During the famous voyage of the raft *Kon-Tiki,* which drifted for three months across the Pacific, Thor Heyerdahl and his colleagues had an unusual opportunity for studying the life of the sea. They were moving in complete silence, and so did not frighten the creatures around them; and as they were level with the water, they could observe everything that came to the surface. The night sea, they reported, was alive with fish never seen during the day, and the darker the night the greater the activity. Strange luminous shapes were moving all around and below, some of them larger than the raft itself.

This suggests that one of the best tools for investigating the unknown life of the sea would not be an expensive submarine or bathyscape, but a simple raft drifting with the current, fitted with lures and baits of various kinds. Manning such a raft, however, might be a dangerous undertaking. The real kraken cannot overwhelm ships and snatch sailors off their decks, as the ancients believed, but an angry giant squid could be a very unpleasant customer to tackle from a raft at sea level.

But would such a creature be really dangerous if one met it face to face? Many of the old perils of the deep have been very much diminished since skin-diving became popular. Only a few years ago, the idea of swimming among sharks and packs of barracuda would have seemed insanity. Today, thousands do it without a second thought, and the number of divers actually killed by marine animals is extremely small. It would be surprising if it is as many as ten a year — a negligible fraction of the number killed through carelessness or accident on land. Most sea animals, even the fiercest hunters of the deep, are very wary of strange invaders of their realm and will seldom attack an unfamiliar object. Hans Hass, the famous underwater explorer, has met the great sperm whale in the open sea, and the scourge of the giant squids gave one nervous glance at the strange little midget flippering through the water with its clicking camera, and promptly took off for parts unknown.

And consider the octopus, that good old stand-by of diving tales. I have never heard of an octopus attacking a skin-diver, but the opposite happens every day. Some tough divers in the Pacific Northwest have invented what must be one of the most rugged hobbies in the world — octopus wrestling. With their bare hands they tackle octopods up to twenty feet across, and bring them back to the surface. According to the rules of the game, the octopus mustn't be hurt, and must be put back unharmed for the next diver to play with. So far, there have been no casualties, although it is hard to understand why.

Perhaps the giant squid, for all its ferocious appearance, may be as shy and retiring as its cousin, the octopus. Nobody can say, and it will be a brave man who first puts the matter to the test.

This may be a good point to make clear the difference

GIANT
SQUID

OCTOPUS

between the squid and the octopus, for many people confuse
the two. The squid has a streamlined body, rather like a fat
torpedo, with two horizontal flukes or fins in front. Its great
eyes are at the rear, from which springs the cluster of eight
tentacles and two long feelers. It is a very good swimmer,
usually traveling tailfirst with its arms trailing behind.
However, it can move in any direction in an emergency, by
squirting out a stream of water from a swiveling flexible tube
which gives it a very effective form of jet propulsion.

The octopus has no streamlining, and its body is a flabby
bag. It has only eight tentacles and is not a particularly
good swimmer. Although it can make a fair speed with its

jet propulsion equipment, it soon becomes tired. Both the squid and the octopus have a neat way of dodging enemies. When hard-pressed, they can eject a cloud of ink, known as sepia. It was once thought that this ink served as a smoke screen, blinding the pursuer, but actually it has quite a different purpose. It serves as a decoy, for the hunter chases after the cloud of ink which clings together in the water and takes some time to disperse, while the octopus makes a sharp turn and shoots off at right angles, changing color at the same instant to improve the deception.

I can testify, from personal experience, that this trick is highly effective. A small octopus once used it on me. I was chasing it over the sea bed — merely intending to make friends — and was reaching out to grab it when the creature literally disappeared. All I had in my hands was the cloud of sepia, and I never saw which way the octopus went. I swam back to shore in a very thoughtful mood, because I knew all about this trick and until then had considered myself brighter than the fish who were deceived by it.

Although there is now no doubt about the giant squid, many naturalists deny the existence of the giant octopus. This may be because scientists are more familiar with waters of the South Pacific and the Mediterranean, where an octopus with a spread of ten feet (that is, with arms five feet long) is exceptionally large. In the cold waters of the Pacific Northwest, particularly in Puget Sound, they grow to much greater size, and the record is a specimen thirty-two feet across the tentacles. This one was caught in a fishing net, from which it probably took some untangling.

Even this is a baby compared with the monster which may have been cast ashore at Saint Augustine, Florida, only a few miles from that fascinating establishment, Marineland, whose curator, Mr. F. G. Wood, has kindly passed the following information on to me. In November, 1896, the remains of a large animal were found embedded in the sands on a beach twelve miles south of Saint Augustine. It weighed about five tons and was some twenty feet long, but was badly mutilated and obviously much of it was missing.

From photographs, and the evidence of naturalists on the spot, Professor A. E. Verrill, the leading expert on giant squids, decided that the creature was an octopus, and from the fragment left, he calculated that its tentacles must have been seventy-five to a hundred feet long. This is about six times the size of the largest octopus ever caught, and it is not surprising that Professor Verrill later had second thoughts and decided that it must have been some other animal — although he couldn't say what. So the mystery remains unsolved to this day.

It is very hard to set a limit to the size that animals can reach in the sea, where the buoyancy of the water supports their weight. On land, of course, gravity is a deciding factor. Very large animals are clumsy and slow moving, and a creature more than two or three times the size of an elephant would collapse under its own weight. Some of the dinosaurs must have come close to the practical limit, and the very largest specimens probably spent most of their time in swamps and rivers, at least partly afloat.

Even in the sea, however, very great size has its disadvantages, and the most important of these is summed up in one word — food. The hundred-ton blue whale can attain its enormous bulk because it literally swims through nourishment in the rich antarctic plankton fields. It has merely to keep its mouth open, and food slides down its throat by the ton.

The deeper we go down into the sea, however, the scarcer food becomes, and the more difficult it would be for really large animals to find enough to eat. In chapter six, you will remember, we explained how all the nourishment in the sea, upon which its swarming multitudes depend, is produced in the upper two or three hundred feet of water which sunlight penetrates. The creatures living below this level must rely upon fragments of food filtering down from above, like hungry dogs fighting over the scraps from a banquet table.

This is one reason why, up to a hundred years ago, it was believed by all scientists that there could be no life really deep down in the sea. There would be nothing to eat in the cold, eternal darkness. We now know that this is wrong. There is quite a lot of life, even on sea beds four or five miles down. But the fish living at this depth are usually very small — only a few inches long — and have huge mouths and elastic stomachs so that they can take advantage of the rare scraps of food that come their way. They are incredibly hideous, but they are certainly not monsters except in appearance.

If there are still unknown giants in the sea, they will not be far down in the abyss, but at more modest depths where food is still fairly plentiful. The big squids appear to flourish one or two thousand feet below the surface. This may be the region which will produce the greatest surprises when we begin to explore it. It is the feeding ground of the sperm whale and there may be other mighty hunters down there, still completely unknown to us.

Is the Great Sea Serpent among them? This fabulous beast has tantalized science for more than a hundred years, and even today no one can be certain whether it exists, or whether it is a complete myth. Perhaps ninety-five per cent of the reported sightings are hoaxes or mistakes in identification. There are so many strange beasts in the oceans that no one could hope to recognize them all, and untrained observers can be easily baffled by a glimpse of some unusual but quite well-known animal. A dying squid, thrashing on the surface, would be enough to convince most people that they had seen the sea serpent — so would a large oarfish, an extraordinary, snakelike creature with a fragile body which may be thirty feet in length. The oarfish has a feathery crest on its back which it can erect when frightened, making it look even more impressive and peculiar. Only a few men have ever seen one alive, but dead specimens are occasionally washed ashore, and there seems little doubt that this strange fish must be responsible for numerous sea serpent reports.

Yet this still leaves many sightings unexplained. Sometimes they have been made by trained naturalists, or by experienced observers who have spent many years at sea and are familiar with all the ordinary marine beasts. Most of the reports agree in describing a large animal — although no larger than a blue whale — which can rear its head out of the water on an eellike neck. It is a powerful swimmer, and usually makes off at high speed before it can be approached.

There are few reports of sea serpents nowadays, which may seem a good reason for disbelieving in them. But we must remember that the propellers of a modern ship make so much underwater noise that no nervous animal would come within miles of it. You can travel for weeks on a large ocean liner without seeing any of the countless common sea animals, except for a few flying fish or an occasional porpoise. The ocean around you is teeming with life, but you would never guess it. And because of the ridicule they are likely to face, few people would admit meeting a sea serpent even if they were quite sure they had done so.

The name "sea serpent" is rather unfortunate, for if such animals do exist, they are almost certainly not serpents —

that is, air-breathing reptiles. There *are* snakes in the sea, beautifully marked and often extremely poisonous, but they seldom exceed four or five feet in length.

Some of the reports suggest that the sea serpent may be a mammal like the whales and porpoises. It is often referred to as having hair, which no fish or reptiles possess. But mammals are air-breathing, and so cannot dive far or stay down for very long. They could never be permanent inhabitants of the deep sea. It seems unlikely that a large, unknown animal living near the surface could have escaped discovery for so long if it really existed.

A possible explanation of the sea serpent turned up in 1930, when the Danish research ship *Dana* made a very startling discovery. For centuries, men have been baffled by the life history of the common fresh-water eel, which is often found in ponds miles from any other water, and which was never known to lay eggs or to have any young. Not until as recently as 1922 was the mystery finally solved, and we know now that the common eel is born far out in the Atlantic, deep beneath the Sargasso Sea — that strange, weed-covered body of water in the central Atlantic, between Africa and the West Indies. The extraordinary story of the eel's migrations from ocean to land and back again to breed does not concern us here. The important point is that newborn eels are not at all eellike. They are transparent little fish, so thin and flattened that you can see right through them, and are shaped like a leaf. Not until they have grown to a length of two or three inches, do eel larvae begin to change into their familiar adult form, in much the same way as tadpoles turn into frogs.

After this introduction, you will now be able to appreciate the *Dana's* remarkable discovery. Eel larvae, as we have said, grow to about three inches in length before changing into adult eels, and a large adult may be five feet long (two feet is nearer the average). The *Dana*, however, fished up an eel larva six feet long — twenty-four times the normal size! This is rather like finding a tadpole a yard long — in both cases the first question one would ask is, "Whatever size is this baby going to be when it grows up?"

Simple arithmetic suggests that a six-foot eel larva would produce an adult forty or fifty feet long. If this is correct, we need look no further for the Great Sea Serpent.

Settling the matter once and for all is not going to be easy. To catch — even to find — large, powerful animals in the depths of the sea will require a great deal of time, money, scientific skill, and luck. Underwater TV, which is so valuable in other fields of research, may be no use at all. The powerful lights would probably attract thousands of small fish, but larger animals would keep their distance. Though fish tend to be attracted by weak lights, very powerful ones are more likely to scare them away. Dr. Beebe discovered this during his bathysphere descents. Several times he saw very large creatures swimming just outside the range of his lights, and was unable to identify them however much he strained his eyes.

One expensive, but possibly effective, way of making a census of the deep would be a freely floating camera. It would carry bait to attract fish, and might be covered with a pattern of colored lights, winking on and off, for in the eternal darkness of the abyss many creatures use weak lights to attract their mates — and their meals. The camera, in its armored case, would drift along the deep-sea currents, and when any large animal approached, its presence would be detected by a simple, short-range sonar set. At the right moment, an electronic flash would fire, and the startled sea monster would have its photograph taken. When all the film was exposed, the camera would float back to the surface and signal its presence by radio or sonar so that it could be picked up.

Photographs are very useful, and will solve many of the mysteries of the deep. But if unknown marine monsters exist, naturalists will never be happy until they have caught them — preferably alive. One way of doing this, which is now being studied, is a giant net which will be sunk by means of heavy weights at its center. At the right depth, the weights will be released and the net will rush upward like a parachute, but in the other direction owing to the buoyancy of floats around its rim. If the net is big enough — diameters of several hundred feet are proposed — and moves quickly enough, it may come to the surface with some spectacular hauls. It may also come up — as has happened often in the past — with a gaping hole through which some powerful animal has made its escape.

The Great Sea Serpent has eluded us for five thousand years, and may keep us at bay for a little longer. But we are sending our first scouts into its secret kingdom, and it cannot hide forever — even in the 300 million cubic miles of the ocean wilderness.

chapter 11

The Book of the Past

THE history of the world lies buried at the bottom of the sea. The ocean bed is a book which we are just beginning to read — or, rather, to decipher, for it is written in a strange language, and many of its myriad pages are missing. Others are still being written, carrying a record of our present age which, perhaps, scientists from distant worlds may read a million years from now.

The pages of this book are made of rather dull substances — muds and oozes. In this case, however, they are anything but dull, for they tell of sunken continents, of volcanic eruptions which must have darkened the skies of earth, of mighty ice fields grinding down from the poles, and of the beginning of life itself upon our planet.

To us, the dry land with its hills and mountains seems eternal, but every drop of rain that returns to the sea takes with it some of the solid earth beneath our feet. Century by century, even the mightiest mountain ranges are worn away. The Rockies and Himalayas that we know are mere ghosts of their former selves, and one day they will have disappeared completely.

The sediment swept out to sea forms vast layers of mud over the continental shelves, but the deeper parts of the ocean are covered with a different kind of carpet. This is formed by the skeletons, made of lime or silica, of trillions upon trillions of tiny plankton plants and animals raining down eternally from the watery heights above. Although these creatures are almost invisibly small, they exist in such countless numbers that their remains have built up mile-thick layers of ooze or clay on the sea bed. When this ooze hardens, it becomes chalk or limestone, so every hill or cliff made of these rocks was formed at the bottom of the sea.

Rachel Carson, in her famous book, *The Sea Around Us,* called this perpetual downward drift of tiny skeletons "the long snowfall," and the phrase gives a good mental picture of the steadily-thickening carpet covering the bottoms of all the oceans of the world. The empty shells and skeletons are also as beautifully and intricately fashioned as any snowflakes. Unlike snowflakes, however, they are almost eternal. When they have settled to the sea bed, they can there remain for a thousand million years.

In some parts of the Atlantic the carpet of sediment is more than two miles thick. It takes several thousand years to build up a layer only one inch deep, so this means that the "long snowfall" has lasted at least 500 million years. It also means that the Atlantic has been an ocean for all this length of time. By comparison, most continents and mountain ranges are creations of yesterday.

During the last twenty years scientists have devoted much effort to obtaining samples of this deep-sea carpet. Coring devices have been invented which can punch holes in the sea bed and bring up continuous tubes of sediment as much as a hundred feet in length. When the value of the ships, equipment, and man power involved in getting them is added up, these cores have probably cost their weight in gold. They are worth it, for they open a door into the unknown past.

When a tree trunk is sawed through, you can see that it is built up layer by layer in concentric rings, each ring representing the growth in one year. For this reason, it is

a simple matter to find the age of a tree merely by counting rings. The experts, however, can do much more than this. Seasons of drought or of heavy rainfall thousands of years ago can be pinpointed by the thickness of the rings. In a bad year, there is scarcely any growth — in a good one, the tree puts on an extra-thick layer.

Something similar happens at the bottom of the sea, except that here the time scale is measured in centuries instead of years. A geologist can work along a core punched from the ocean bed, and can watch the coming and going of the Ice Ages. At one level, for example, there will be the skeletons of creatures that live only in tropical seas. A few inches away — that is, ten or twenty thousand years further back in the past — the skeletons are those of cold-water animals. And here there may be pebbles and grits that can only have come from the land — how did they reach this point, a thousand miles from the nearest shore? Icebergs carried them here when they calved off the glaciers covering the frozen continents; as they melted, they dumped these souvenirs from distant lands.

By such patient detective work, the geologists can study climatic changes that occurred before the first man walked the earth. And recently they have been able to do something even more marvelous. They have been able to measure the actual temperature of the ocean, hundreds of thousands of years ago. When you stop to think about it, such a feat seems absolutely incredible. Without a time machine, there would seem to be no way of going back into the past and dipping a thermometer into some primeval sea.

This miraculous piece of scientific detection has been made possible by a very delicate chemical analysis of certain shells taken from the deep-sea cores. The rate at which shells absorb elements from the sea water around them depends upon the temperature, just as the rate of growth of tree rings depends upon the rainfall. And so it is now possible to draw a graph of the rise and fall of the thermometer in seas that rolled a million years ago.

And here is another secret of the past which has been wrested from the clay and ooze of the sea bed: Which way did the compass point in 500,000 B.C.? A few years ago, no one would have dreamed that such a question could ever be answered. But today, by studying the direction in which various magnetic substances have come to point as they drifted to the sea bed, we are able to study the movement of the earth's magnetic poles, thousands of years before the compass was invented — or there were any men to use it.

It may not sound very romantic to call the sea a cosmic garbage dump, but the debris of land, air, and even space is continually drifting down into its depths. At this moment, we are contributing to it in no small way. Every diver has come across empty bottles and cans, burned out electric bulbs, lost anchors, old boots — the list is endless and includes practically every object that man has ever made. But long before men sailed the ocean, nature was dumping her rubbish into the waves, and we have been able to learn a great deal from the trash of centuries that has gathered on the sea bed. One recent discovery which may be of extreme importance — although its exact meaning is still unknown — is that huge areas of the Pacific and Atlantic are covered with layers of volcanic ash. Judging from its depth in the sediment, this ash was deposited about seventy thousand years ago. Some titanic eruption must have taken place then, perhaps one violent enough to have produced major changes in the geography of the earth.

Just now we mentioned debris from space — yes, that lies on the sea bed, although in very minute quantities. Meteors are continually raining down upon our planet, and most of them fall into the sea. So occasionally tiny globules of meteor dust are discovered in some marine sediments. There may be many very large meteors in the sea as well, but we have not yet found them.

There must be some areas of the ocean where there are no currents or earthquakes to disturb the eternal submarine snowfall, and where the entire history of the last few billion years lies in layer upon layer waiting to be read, with all the pages intact and in their correct order. On land, the geological record is never complete, for the rocks which carry the messages of the past are themselves being continually worn away, and are often broken or overturned by the movements of the continents. Getting at that sunken history book, two or three miles below the surface, is one of the greatest tasks facing the oceanographers.

Today's hundred-foot cores merely scratch the surface of the deep-sea sediment. They span only a million years of its history. How can we obtain a sample through its entire thickness which may be as much as twelve thousand feet? This is still an unsolved problem in underwater engineering, but a daring attempt to do this — and more — is now being planned by scientists in the United States and the Soviet Union.

We have already mentioned, in chapter nine, the successful drilling of oil wells on the sea bed from boats anchored offshore. It is believed that the same technique can be used to drill holes not only through the sediments on the ocean bed, but also clear through the outer crust of the earth itself.

During the next few years, you are going to hear a good deal about this plan to drill a hole through the sea bed into the earth's interior. It will cost as much as a space satellite, and will lead to discoveries of equal importance, because for the first time it will give us samples of the unknown stuff of which our planet is made. And if it also provides the geologists with a complete section through the billion or more years of sediment on the ocean bed, it will allow them to look back into time, almost as dramatically as the satellites have enabled the astronomers to look out into space.

Just as there are layers in the sky, like the famous Heaviside Layer which reflects radio waves, and the recently discovered Van Allen radiation belts, so there are layers of various kinds within the earth. They were first detected by a study of earthquake records, for earthquakes send vibrations racing back and forth inside the solid body of our globe, and by measuring their time of arrival, scientists have been able to construct a kind of X-ray picture of the earth.

In this way, a Yugoslavian scientist named Mohorivicic discovered a dividing layer — or discontinuity — between the familiar rocks which make up the outer crust of our planet and the denser material which extends all the way to the earth's core, some two thousand miles down. Since it takes several seconds' hard work to say "Mohorivicic discontinuity," even when you know how, the abbreviation Moho is universally used for this layer.

The Moho is not at the same depth everywhere. Under the land, it is about twenty miles down — far deeper than any well can be drilled, for the record at the moment is only five miles. But under the sea, it is much closer to us, sometimes only three miles below the ocean bed, or a total of six miles down from sea level. It is not surprising, therefore, that scientists are excited at the idea of using the new underwater drilling techniques to break through to the earth's interior, so tantalizingly close at hand.

Let us stop to think what this may mean. As the long tubes of densely packed sediment are brought up to the

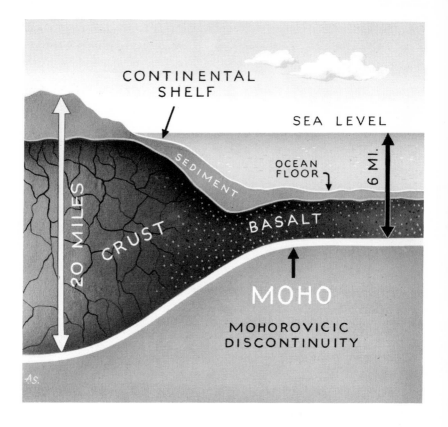

CONTINENTAL SHELF

SEA LEVEL

OCEAN FLOOR

6 MI.

SEDIMENT

20 MILES

CRUST

BASALT

MOHO

MOHOROVICIC DISCONTINUITY

surface, we shall be boring back through the ages, just as the archaeologists who excavated Troy peeled away the centuries, layer by layer, to find that one city had been built upon another. But Troy was only a moment ago. We may be going back a million times further into the unknown past. The first cores will repeat the story of the Ice Ages that we have already traced, and for awhile we will be drilling our way through familiar eras of time. Every foot of the core will represent perhaps fifty thousand years of prehistory, and soon the head of the drill will be passing through layers that settled to the bed of the ocean when the great reptiles ruled the earth.

Yet even that is not so long ago, in the immense vistas of geological time. The last of the dinosaurs perished some sixty million years ago, and the earth may be a hundred times as old as this. As the drill works its way backwards into the records of the rocks, the fragments of shells and skeletons it brings up will belong to ever more primitive creatures — perhaps creatures so close to the beginning of life that we have found no trace of them on land. And at some point, corresponding to a time about a billion years ago, there will be a change in the material brought up. It will no longer contain fragments of once-living creatures, for the drill will have gone past the moment when life appeared on earth. We will be looking at our world as it was before a single blade of grass waved on land, or a single primitive jellyfish drifted in the sea.

Like the reader of a mystery story who has turned most of the pages of the book and is now rushing headlong toward its ending, we, too, will be about to unravel a secret. It will be one of the greatest of all secrets, that of life itself, and the way it began on earth.

Below this level there will be only the record of the winds and rains and volcanoes as they carved and molded the empty earth, preparing it for the dramas still to come. When our questing drills reach this depth, they will enter a world we would not recognize. They may reach the original surface of our planet, as it was in the days when it was formed. And so we will have traveled back in time not only to the coming of life, but beyond that to the origin of the earth.

Perhaps you feel a little dizzy after contemplating these endless vistas of time — not mere millions, but billions of years. So let us come a little closer to our own age, and to history as we know it.

Since man started to sail the seas, at least five thousand

years ago, he has had to pay a heavy price for the privilege. There is a ship sinking somewhere even as you read these words. It may be a humble fishing boat off an unchartered Pacific island, or a great liner plunging beneath the waves in the busy Atlantic. Millions of ships, carrying no small part of the total wealth of mankind, have sunk in the past, and many more will sink in the future despite all our scientific skill and technical aids.

What happens to a ship and its cargo when it goes down depends upon the depth of the water and the nature of the sea bed. Most ships are lost when they run aground, relatively few sink in the open sea. A wreck in shallow water seldom lasts for more than a few years before the waves tear it to pieces and scatter its cargo far and wide over the sea bed. This is why the search for the millions of dollars of gold lost in the Spanish treasure ships has been so unrewarding. The gold is still there at a depth that a skin-diver could reach without breathing equipment — but the ships that carried it have been smashed into fragments centuries ago, and the fragments themselves covered with such a coating of coral that no one could recognize them.

I have seen this process in action, myself. A few years ago a medium-sized freighter went aground on the west coast of Ceylon, some miles from where I am writing this, and for a month or so its funnel and bridge were well above the water line. Then came the monsoon storms, racing across the Indian Ocean from Africa, and in a few days all the superstructure of the ship was torn away. A year later I explored the wreck underwater, and was glad to get out because the decks had come adrift and were floating up and down with each passing wave, while the hull itself was creaking and groaning around me. In a few more years, nothing will be left except the massive propeller, and in a generation or so even that will have worked its way into the sea bed and be buried beneath marine growths.

It is a different story when a ship sinks in moderately deep water, below the reach of the waves. Then it can survive intact for many years — sometimes for centuries. Today's echo-sounders have drawn, clear and sharp on their charts, the wreck of the torpedoed *Lusitania*, still standing upright on the sea bed three hundred feet down where she has been resting since 1915. And what is probably the most famous of all wrecks, the *Titanic*, is so deep in the unchanging abyss of the Atlantic that she may well outlast the civilization that built her.

In the right circumstances, the sea is a safer place for treasures than the land. This has been demonstrated in the Mediterranean, where some of the most splendid of all the bronze and marble statues of the Greek artists have been found by divers. Where the mud has covered these lost masterpieces, they have been so perfectly preserved that they seem to have come straight from the workshop. If they had been on land, weather or invading armies would have destroyed them centuries ago.

The bed of the Mediterranean must have concealed within it more treasures from Greek and Roman times than are in all the museums in the world. Since the invention of the Aqua-lung made underwater archaeology practical on a wide scale, dozens of wrecks, many dating from before the birth of Christ, have been uncovered, and their cargoes brought back to the surface. Some were heavily laden freighters carrying several hundred tons of grain, oil or wine stored in thousands of the pointed clay jars — amphorae — which were the universal containers of antiquity. Many of these jars are still sealed, with their contents intact — though Captain Cousteau, who has tasted some, tells us that wine does not improve when it is kept for two thousand years.

It is an amazing fact that we even know the names of the merchants who shipped some of these lost cargoes, back in 200 B.C. And, as a sad proof that in many ways human nature does not change, some wine jars have counterfeit seals on them where an exporter, more than twenty centuries dead, has tried to deceive his customers by selling them an inferior vintage.

Yet perhaps the most astonishing find from these ancient wrecks is not one of the magnificent statues that are now the pride of the Athens museum, but a few pieces of corroded bronze that most people would have thrown back into the sea without a second thought. They were discovered in 1900 by sponge divers off the Greek island of Antikythera, and it has taken half a century to uncover their extraordinary secret — for they are nothing less than the fragments of an elaborate calculating machine, containing a mass of gear-wheels which controlled a set of graduated scales rather like clock dials. From the inscriptions on the device, it was clearly designed to predict the movements of the sun, moon and planets. What is almost unbelievable is that it is more complicated than any machine known to exist until two or three hundred years ago. Yet it is over two thousand years old, for it can be dated rather accurately at around 80 B.C.

We have always known that the greatest intellects of all time lived in Greece several centuries before Christ, but it had been believed that their achievements were in mathematics and philosophy, rather than mechanics. Now it seems that before their civilization collapsed, the Greeks had built machines that were not equaled again until the eighteenth century.

The Antikythera mechanism is something that Benjamin Franklin might have built for the astonishment of his scientifically-minded friends. We would not have expected to come across it in any earlier period. Yet here it is, preserved by a miracle on the bottom of the Mediterranean, tantalizing proof of a highly developed technology two thousand years ago.

History is full of Ifs and Might Have Beens — this, surely, is one of the greatest. If the civilization that built this long-lost computer had progressed at the same rate as our Western culture, we would have explored all the planets and been outward bound to the stars — several centuries before the Battle of Hastings.

Although most underwater archaeology has so far taken place in the Mediterranean, there is plenty of scope elsewhere. A very interesting recent project has been the attempt of Ed Link, inventor of the well-known Link Trainer for aviators, to locate the wreck of the *Santa Maria*, which went aground on a reef off Haiti on Christmas Eve, 1492. Probably more ships have been involved in mishaps on Christmas Day than any other. The whole crew of the *Santa Maria* was sleeping off its celebrations, and only a boy was at the helm when she hit the reef. Today, such a performance would have cost Columbus his master's certificate.

Using underwater metal detectors, and all possible modern electronic aids, Ed Link has found a large anchor which is of the correct type and period for the *Santa Maria*, and one day parts of the ship herself may be located — as, recently, the timbers of the almost equally famous *Bounty* were discovered where mutineers had destroyed her off Pitcairn Island in 1789.

But the ocean has swallowed more than ships, for in the eternal war between sea and land, villages and towns and even countries have been overwhelmed by the waves. In all parts of the world, there are rumors of sunken lands and stories of great floods. Most of them are pure myths, but some are based on reality.

In the Mediterranean, once again, divers are now busily at work exploring the remains of submerged towns and sea-ports. These are in quite shallow water, at depths of fifty to a hundred feet, and how they got there is something of a mystery, for the level of the Mediterranean has scarcely altered for thousands of years. Probably earthquakes were responsible, for several cases are known of coastal towns that have sunk beneath the sea within the space of a few hours, taking all their inhabitants with them. One of the most famous is the drowned city of Port Royal, the pirate-infested capital of Jamaica which was destroyed in 1692. With it sank — according to some reports — a fortune in loot, but it is not likely that anyone will ever make much profit by hauling it up. Salvage operations are expensive at the best of times, and any bucaneers' gold at Port Royal must by now be buried so deeply beneath two and a half centuries of coral that it would be cheaper to mine new bullion from the land. The examination of sunken cities is valuable be-cause of what it may tell us about lost chapters of history — not because of what we may salvage from them.

Of all lost lands, there is one whose name has haunted mankind for centuries. This is the fabled empire of Atlantis, supposed to have flourished some ten thousand years ago. Practically the whole of the evidence for its existence was written by the Greek philosopher, Plato, about 350 B.C. Unfortunately, we are not sure whether Plato meant us to take him seriously, or whether his story was merely a kind of parable — a form of early science fiction. But many peo-ple have taken it as literal truth, which is rather like someone in the year 4000 assuming that George Orwell's novel, *1984*, is an accurate account of conditions at that time. Of course, it may be — but we all hope not!

What Plato actually says about Atlantis can be summed

up very briefly. He describes it as a great and wealthy empire "west of the Pillars of Hercules" which had conquered most of the nations of the Mediterranean, including the Greeks, around the year 9000 B.C. Although at first they were just and upright, the Atlanteans eventually became corrupt and decadent, and Zeus decided to punish them. And so "there occurred violent earthquakes and floods, and in a single day and night of rain . . . the island of Atlantis disappeared and was sunk beneath the sea." You will notice the parallel with the Old Testament story of the flood. There was, however, no Atlantean Noah.

On this slender basis, hundreds of books have been written, and men have devoted their entire lives to unraveling the truth about Atlantis. Unfortunately, most of the literature on the subject is not merely worthless — it is misleading nonsense produced by cranks. This is a great pity, for the legend of Atlantis may well be based on truth, and serious students have been scared away from it by the crackpots.

Eleven thousand years is a very long time, but there were highly cultured races of mankind twenty or thirty thousand years ago, as is proved by the beautiful cave paintings that have been found in Spain and France. And since there have been so many towns and even whole islands swallowed by the sea, Plato's account is completely plausible, even though he certainly exaggerated for the sake of effect when he described the great city of Atlantis with its buildings ornamented with gold, silver and brass.

If Atlantis ever did exist in reality, where should we look for its ruins today? We can be fairly sure of one thing — that it is *not* on the bed of the Atlantic. As the record of the deep-sea sediments has proved, the Atlantic Ocean has been in much its present position for hundreds of millions of years. True, there have been local ups and downs in more

THE FABLED EMPIRE

recent times, but it is virtually certain that no really large island has existed there since the coming of man.

Although Plato tells us that Atlantis was "west of the Pillars of Hercules" (the Straits of Gibraltar) this might only mean that the Atlanteans came through the straits. The ancient Greeks were extremely bad sailors — despite all the tall tales of Ulysses — and never ventured out into the Atlantic Ocean. To them, the western seas were a place of mystery and danger, as they still were until the age of Columbus, two thousand years later. So the Atlanteans could have come from Africa, or even from North or South America. The real Atlantis might never have sunk at all. If its people lost the spirit of adventure and ceased to sail

into the Mediterranean, the disappearance of their ships might have inspired the legend that their country had likewise vanished.

It is also quite possible that we have been looking for Atlantis in the wrong place, for there is evidence that to the early Greeks the Pillars of Hercules did not mean the Straits of Gibraltar at all. If you look at a map of the Mediterranean, you will see a narrow gap between the toe of Italy and the island of Sicily. This is the Strait of Messina, one of the most dangerous passages in the world because of its furious tide races. Some archaeologists believe that this was the place originally meant by the term Pillars of Hercules, and if so it would locate Atlantis in the western basin of the Mediterranean, perhaps between Italy and Sardinia.

Now this makes a good deal of sense. The Mediterranean is a new sea, not an ancient ocean like the Atlantic or Pacific which have both existed for millions of years. Men were alive when the bed of the Mediterranean was a fertile valley, and Spain met Africa to form a barrier against the Atlantic.

Many geologists believe that this barrier went down some twelve thousand years ago, which agrees very well with the date given by Plato for the fall of Atlantis. It probably took many years for the water to come flooding in through the breach — certainly it did not happen overnight — but the legend of the catastrophe would have been made more dramatic as it was passed down by storytellers, generation after generation.

There are many other theories — almost as many as there are books — and it would be unwise to take any one of them too seriously in the light of present knowledge. But it would be equally unwise to dismiss this story, which has such a remarkable power over the imagination of mankind, as a complete myth. Only a hundred years ago Troy was considered to be a legend with no reality behind it. We know better now. And one day we shall know the truth about Atlantis, as our exploration of the sea bed fills the great blanks in the maps of the ocean floor.

Whether Atlantis existed or not, other continents have sunk beneath the waves. To us short-lived creatures the world seems a solid and unchanging place, but deep down in the earth immense forces are forever at work altering the pattern of land and sea. We would not even recognize our world if we could look down on it from space, as it was a hundred million years ago — or as it will be a hundred million years from now. Land and sea have changed places many times in the past, and there is no reason to suppose that they will not do so again.

Lovely are the names that have been given to these lost continents that vanished ages before the first man walked the earth. Lemuria, Gondwanaland, Nearctis, Llanoria, Appalachia, Cascadia. . . . There is a magic about them, as of Keats' "perilous seas, in faery lands forlorn." Some may be no more than fantasies invented by geologists to support one theory or another, and will vanish in the light of later knowledge. But others must have existed, and must have seen the coming and going of the monstrous beasts that lived when the world was young.

And sometimes we wonder if they may have seen more than this. We are now about to begin the exploration of the universe — but surely, in the billions of years that lie behind us, many other races must have done the same. In the aeons before history began, how often have strange ships thundered down through the skies of Earth to terrify the dinosaurs or to set the flowerless trees waving with the wind of their passage?

If they ever came, those ancient explorers must have left traces. Somewhere they must have dumped their empty bottles and food containers, their burned-out electron tubes and dead batteries, their broken machines and instruments.

If we ever find such things, fossilized thousands of feet down in the deep-sea sediments, what a shattering effect it will have upon our thoughts and beliefs! Overnight, our outlook on the universe will change completely, and we will look up at the starry sky with new feelings. For we will at last have proof that our earth is not the only home of intelligence, and we will know that if we once had visitors from space — they may one day come again.

chapter 12

The Submarine Playground

MAN does not live by bread alone, and that will still be true even when most of his nourishment comes from the sea. In this book we have talked about all the practical and scientific uses of the oceans. Now the time has come to complete the picture, and to recognize that the sea will be one of the great playgrounds of tomorrow — a place for relaxation, amusement and adventure.

To some extent, of course, it has always been so, but until a few years ago all our enjoyment of the sea was confined to its surface. Swimming, surfing, pleasure-boating — these are activities that involve only the first few feet of water. And they will continue into the future as far as our imagination can go. When there is no more surface transportation on our planet, and all our traffic moves through the skies, there will still be myriad white sails billowing above the waves. Ten thousand years from now — unless men have changed out of all recognition — our descendants will still be building boats whose only purpose is to give their masters that mingling of power and peace that comes when one is driving silently before the wind, over a sparkling sea.

It is our great good fortune to be born in the age that opened the door into the sea. Yet we have never really escaped from it. The salts in our bloodstream still reflect its chemical composition. Our minds still respond to the call, heard clearly across a billion years of time, from the empty oceans of the dawn in which all life began. And now at last we have discovered how to re-enter, for as long or short a period as we wish, the element in which we were born.

We might have done so several centuries ago. It's an ironic thought that the mask, breathing tube, and flippers of the modern skin-diver were all depicted in the notebooks of the fantastic genius, Leonardo da Vinci. Yet until our generation, for want of a piece of glass and a few square inches of rubber, men have swum blind amidst beauty, have been strangers peering through a distorting mirror into a world which they could never fully enter. For the human eye is unable to focus when it is in direct contact with water, and a diver without a mask is almost blind. But when he wears a face mask, his eyes are in air and can therefore focus normally. He can see everything around him, just as clearly as if he is looking into an aquarium.

No sport in history has ever grown as rapidly as underwater exploring. At first much of the emphasis was on spear fishing, but now there are many who are content to enter the submarine world as peaceful and passive spectators, wishing only to observe its wonders and keep on good terms with its inhabitants. Everyone who goes underwater becomes an amateur scientist, for so much is new and unexplained in that blue world where the sea plants wave, like trees forever tossing before a silent gale.

Many old myths vanished as men saw with their own eyes where before they had merely guessed. We now know that most of the sea's dangers have been grossly overrated, for men have swum and hunted safely in waters that were once supposed to hold sudden death. Today there is no reason why anyone in normal health should not, after a little instruction, enter the world of wonder and beauty that lies so near at hand, on the other side of the waves.

Only ten years ago it would have seemed a wild fantasy to talk of underwater tourism. But today, guides are conducting sight-seers over reefs and wrecks in the Caribbean, the Mediterranean, the Florida Keys and along the coast of Ceylon. With this beginning, the next stage is obvious. Let us look just a few years ahead, to the time when the techniques and equipment that already exist have led to their logical conclusion. We will pay a visit to an underwater resort of the 1960's.

The hotel seems to grow out of the reef, concrete blending with coral both above and below the water line. But you have to see it from the air, when you can look down into the clear blue depths, before you realize that the greater part of the building is beneath the surface. Ten feet down, running completely around the hotel so that both lagoon and ocean can be surveyed, are the wide observation windows. They are crowded with spectators by day and night, for after sunset, fish in countless thousands are attracted by the glare of the undersea lights.

Nothing is more restful than sitting here in the cool, submarine twilight of the observation room, sipping a drink and watching the strange shapes that come and go on the far side of the glass. But for the greatest thrill that the Reef Hotel can provide, you must become a fish yourself.

There's no danger. The equipment is practically foolproof, and there's never been a serious accident with it. The guides have gone out with tourists of all ages from six to ninety. Some of the sight-seers have come back with mild headaches — but they've all wanted to go out again.

The normal-sized group for an underwater trip is six. Any guide would have difficulty in handling a larger party. The excursions take place around noon, when the sun is at its height and the submarine landscape is most strongly illuminated. There have been a few night expeditions, using powerful searchlights, but these are for the experts only.

Before you dive, you'll have to undergo a routine check by the hotel physician. He'll be mainly interested in your nose and ears, for sinus trouble can result in severe pain as pressure increases, and wax in the ears can also be dangerous. Very few people, however, get eliminated from the trip.

The diving chamber — Neptune's Lobby — is a large, bare room which has to be entered through an air lock. It's thirty feet below the surface, and a wide flight of steps leads from it down into the water. You may have to swallow hard, and blow briskly while holding your nose, before you get used to the pressure. The air here has to be compressed to twice its normal density to keep the water from filling the chamber.

Your guide is a muscular, barrel-chested youngster who is quite prepared to submerge for several minutes without any breathing gear at all. Slowly and carefully he briefs the party, making sure that everyone understands each piece of apparatus as it's fitted on.

First, the flippers. You'll have learned how to use them in the shallow water of the lagoon, and will already know the enormous feeling of confidence it gives to be able to torpedo effortlessly through the water.

Next, the face mask that makes you look and feel like a spaceman. It covers your eyes, nose and mouth, and there's a tiny microphone built into it so that you can talk to your companions. You can hear them through a speaker strapped behind your ear, pressing against the bone.

Finally comes the harness carrying the two small Fiberglas cylinders containing air under enormous pressure. These are

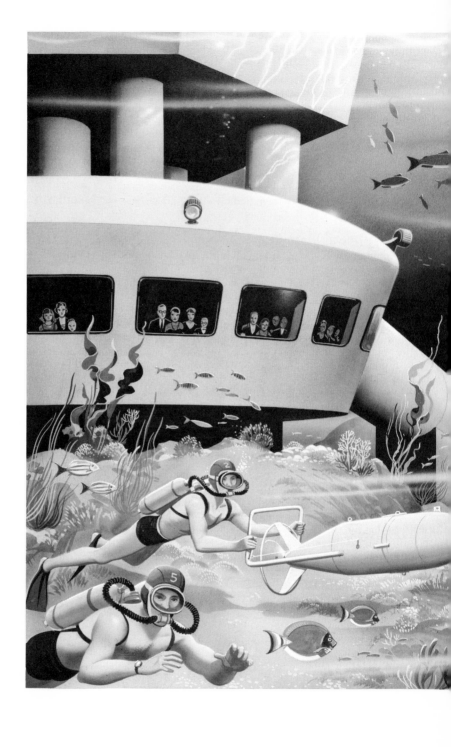

coupled to the regulator, which automatically supplies you with the exact amount of air you require at any depth.

The tiny underwater radio, with a range of about a hundred yards, is also part of the harness. It's not actually a radio, of course, although everyone calls it that. Radio waves will not travel through water for any distance, so this equipment works on very high-frequency sound waves. The guide will use his transmitter to give you instructions and point out objects of interest, but he asks you not to talk back unless he calls you. The sea is no place for idle chatter.

The last adjustment is made. The air begins to hiss through the regulator. At a word from your guide, you slowly and awkwardly waddle down the steps into the still, blue water.

Your weight ebbs away to zero as you submerge. To many people, breaking through the surface of the water while still continuing to breathe requires a definite effort of will. They try to hold their breath until their lungs are bursting, unable to believe that the air supply is still uninterrupted. But after a very few minutes they have forgotten all these fears and are reveling in their new-found freedom.

There is a wide concrete shelf at the foot of the stairs overlooking the exit to the diving chamber. You will spend some minutes here, only a few inches from the reassuring safety of air, while the guide makes his final check and tests the radios. One by one you reply, confirming that your sets are working and that you feel fine. There are some last-minute adjustments to weight belts — a stout gentleman has difficulty in staying down, and needs a couple of extra pounds of lead. Then you are ready to go.

The guide launches himself forward with a slow but powerful kick, and the rest of you follow with varying degrees of skill. You are swimming under the wall that traps the air in the diving chamber. Now you are out in the sunlight — in open water, thirty feet down. Above you, like a silken roof, lies the frontier between sea and air. It is very still for there is hardly any wind. In one place the image of the sun winks and dances in slow explosions of light with the gentle movement of the water.

Effortlessly, with a steady beating of your flippers, you follow the guide. So clear is the water that it's easy to imagine you are really flying, surrounded not by fish but by birds. The illusion is heightened by the sea plants beneath you, which look exactly like small trees or shrubs.

You are now well clear of the hotel. Looking back, you can see the underwater windows from which your friends are doubtless watching you — although you cannot see into the darkened observation chambers. Fish are beginning to swarm around, sometimes swimming right up to your mask to peer inquisitively into your eyes. They have absolutely no fear, for hunting is rigidly forbidden near the hotel. It would scare away the creatures who are the resort's main attraction.

It is true that the guide carries a gun that fires finned, jet-propelled spears with explosive heads. But this is purely for defense in an emergency — he's never had to use it yet. When large fish become too inquisitive he can always drive them away with his electric tickler — a slender rod carrying two probes with a few hundred volts between them.

"We should have company in a few seconds," the guide announces. "They're usually here the moment we leave the diving chamber — in fact, sometimes they come into it and escort us out. Oh, here they are!"

Two grey, streamlined shapes come shooting toward you at an incredible speed. Your heart skips a beat before you recognize Joe and Jill, the hotel's tame porpoises. They circle the expedition several times, then dart swiftly to the surface. Air-breathing animals, they can drown in a few minutes. You realize, rather smugly, that with your Aqualung you can stay underwater ten times as long as they can. On the other hand, you can't swim at forty miles an hour.

There is something about porpoises that restores one's faith in humanity. They actually like men, and while they are around as protection there's no need to worry about sharks. Not that anyone does, for the much-vaunted tiger of the seas is a complete coward who will usually run for his life at the first sign of determined opposition. *Usually.* There are enough exceptions to provide that variety which is the spice of life.

With the porpoises as escort, you glide slowly over the coral, resisting the temptation to pluck the beautifully colored stone flowers that are not flowers at all, but the homes of myriad marine animals.

"Don't touch the live coral," your guide warns. "It can sting badly — particularly that red variety. No one knows what purpose these colors serve, by the way. They still exist a couple of hundred feet down where even the fish can never see them, as the red light has all been filtered out by the water."

Beneath you now is a carefully landscaped coral garden, with ranks of multicolored sea anemones laid out in a pattern which is just regular enough to be pleasing to the eye, but not so regimented that it is obviously artificial. It is a fine example of a new art — underwater gardening. The garden is silent, but never still. The tentacles of the anemones are continually waving with a slow, hypnotic rhythm. The fish move, sometimes languidly, sometimes in sudden darts, back and forth among the branches of the coral. Although the colors here are as brilliant as any on the surface of the earth, if one brought them up into the alien air they would swiftly fade. They can be seen only by those willing to go down among them.

At one end of the coral garden is a concrete bench, shaded by a trelliswork which has been overgrown by marine plants. You sit here in a solemn line, wavering slightly in the gentle current, while your guide gives you another briefing. The sun's rays, streaming through the water overhead, are broken into bands of light which move unpredictably in all directions, covering the painted coral with shifting zebra patterns of light and shade.

"Even with flippers," says your guide, "it's tiring to travel any considerable distance underwater — as you've doubtless noticed. Yet there's some fine scenery around here that we'd like to show you, so we've arranged transport."

He starts to glide away, suddenly notices something, and dives swiftly toward a wall of coral. Thrusting his hand into a crevice, he pulls out a wiggling mass of tentacles and holds it in front of the nervous spectators.

"They're shy beasts," he says, neatly foiling the octopus's desperate attempts to escape. "Look at all the color changes he is going through — they express emotions, and I guess he is pretty frightened now. Anyone else like to play with him?"

There's a profound silence. Nobody seems anxious to volunteer. So the guide releases his captive, which promptly squirts its way back into its hole, leaving behind a cloud of ink as a token of disapproval.

Your guide disappears behind a large, obviously artificial mound, and a moment later a throbbing drone reaches you through the water. A long, slim torpedo slowly rises into sight. The guide is riding it like a jockey, and adjusting the controls on its tiny instrument panel.

"This is one of our hydrojets," he explains. "You can clip

yourselves to these tow ropes and then we'll be ready to go."

Amidships, two horizontal rods project from the vehicle, trailing towing lines so that three passengers can attach themselves on either side. As you clip the buckle to your harness, you feel rather like a husky in a dog team — except for the fact that the traces will be towing *you*.

When everyone has been securely attached, the pilot eases the throttle forward. The vibration of the water jet can be clearly felt, but it's not powerful enough to cause discomfort. With the two porpoises still as escorts, you slowly rise from the sea bed and begin your effortless exploration.

Your radius of vision is more than a hundred feet, although distances are notoriously hard to judge underwater. At the limit of visibility, objects fade into a blue-green haze which first blurs fine detail, then obliterates everything. But up to fifty feet, you can see as clearly as in the open air.

Now a cliff is approaching — a vertical wall climbing out of the gloom below and reaching almost to the sunlit surface. From top to bottom, as far as the eye can see, it is an unbroken sheet of multicolored life. The pilot cuts his motor, and you drift along the face of the cliff while he points out some of the creatures who have made it their home.

Here the distinction between plant and animal has been lost. Here are plants that move in search of prey, and animals that spend their lives rooted to a single spot. And there are extraordinary partnerships — crabs with anemones growing on their claws, large fish with tiny scavengers swimming unmolested in their mouths.

Quite suddenly, darkness falls. For a moment you think that a cloud has passed across the sun. Then, with a shock that almost freezes your heart, you see that an enormous, shadowy shape is floating above you. Before alarm can grow to panic, the guide's voice sounds in your speaker.

"There's nothing to worry about — that's only a whale shark. They are absolutely harmless — they live on minute sea plants and can't even bite. Some of them grow up to sixty feet in length. Notice that characteristic mottled skin. They are true fish, not mammals, like whales — see those huge gills opening and closing? If I harpooned this character he wouldn't even fight back — he'd just swim slowly away. Let's go up and have a better look at him."

You seem to be drifting past a submarine. Surely no living creature could be this big! The shark takes not the slightest notice of the hydrojet and its passengers. The great beast cruises slowly along with a bovine indifference, gills opening and closing like vast venetian blinds. A few tiny pilot fish ride its bow wave, and the monster's body is so encrusted with barnacles that it resembles the hull of a ship. You're now too interested to be scared. You can really believe that the largest fish in the sea is also the most harmless.

The great shadow drifts away, and the sun emerges from eclipse. It's time to turn for home. Already, the expedition has been gone for more than an hour. In a wide arc, banking like an airplane, the hydrojet swings around and the shoals of fish scatter before it. The living cliffs of coral seem to be toppling — you have lost all sense of up or down as you swing at the end of your towline. Then you notice the direction of the sun and realize that you are falling along an invisible slope into deeper water.

"I'm going down to a hundred feet," says the pilot. "Just keep breathing steadily, and swallow hard every few seconds. If anyone's ears start to hurt, we'll come up at once."

The light is changing around you, becoming blue and, curiously, more intense — although that is really an illusion. The reds and oranges that give warmth to the upper world are being leached away by the thickening layers of water overhead. Now you are in the cold twilight on the very frontier of the sunless abyss. It is cold, too, in more senses than one. You have passed out of the warm surface waters and are heading down toward the level where it is never more than a few degrees above freezing.

The pressure over your body is now more than a hundred tons — yet you feel no discomfort and can still breathe perfectly normally, thanks to the regulator on your back. With similar equipment, breathing helium-oxygen mixtures, men have descended more than a thousand feet. Your ambitions, however, fall far short of that. At just below one hundred feet, the hydrojet flattens out and cruises on a level keel for a few minutes.

You can still see the wrinkled surface of the water far overhead, with the mock suns dancing in it. But there are different fish and different colors around you now. Life in the ocean changes with depth, obeying the general rule that each layer of the sea feeds the one below it.

You feel a long way from the world of sun and air, yet the greatest depths of the ocean lie further below you than the peak of Mount Everest towers above. Down there, under a pressure of a thousand tons to the square foot, life still exists. And as the hydrojet begins its slow climb back to the hotel, a sudden wild fancy strikes you.

A century ago, this expedition would have seemed a fantastic dream. But once men have started on a road, they will follow it to its end. So sometime in the 2100's, a guide may be standing in front of a group of tourists, protected by equipment you cannot imagine, and saying, "Well, folks, here we are at the bottom of the Marianas Trench. For your information, there are approximately seven miles of water above us. Now, if you'll just stand back while I deal with this giant squid, we can proceed to the next point of interest."

You are still chuckling over this fantasy — yet is it a fantasy? When the coral garden comes into sight again another party of tourists is sitting on the bench, waiting to take over the hydrojet. Above them two large rays are circling with slow beats of what you can only call their wings, for they look exactly like giant, spotted birds flapping through the sky.

The hydrojet settles down beside its concealed garage, you uncouple your harness, and, once more relying on your own muscles, follow your guide back to the hotel. As you pass the observation windows, you wave gaily to any invisible spectators who may be watching you from inside — and you hope someone's taken your photograph so that you can send it home to your friends.

The hotel's already thought of that, naturally. The prints are waiting for you as soon as you emerge.

And so, in holiday mood, we will take leave of the sea. In this book we have touched upon many of the practical uses of the oceans in the years ahead, and we have glanced at some of the mysteries still awaiting us in the unexplored two-thirds of our planet. Vast industries as yet undreamed of, scientific discoveries that will shake the world — these and many other things will come from the sea to make a happier and richer future for mankind.

But beyond this, the sea has something else to offer. For centuries, it has inspired the greatest deeds of heroism and the greatest works of art. From Homer's *Odyssey*, the Norse sagas, the tales of Melville, Stevenson, Conrad, and later writers such as Herman Wouk or C. S. Forrester — how much of the world's literature we owe to the sea! Yet the poets and novelists of the past saw only one of its faces. What lay beneath the waves was as unknown to them as the far side of the moon.

Perhaps as our knowledge grows, the sea will lose some of its mystery and magic — but I do not think so. As far ahead as imagination can roam, there will be unexplored depths, lonely islands, endless leagues of ocean upon which a lost ship could wander for weeks without sighting land. When the continents have been tamed from pole to pole, when all the deserts have been irrigated, the forests cleared, the polar icecap melted — much of the sea will still remain an untouched wilderness.

Let us hope that it will always be so. In the sea, as nowhere else, a man can find solitude and detachment. There are times when each one of us needs this, just as there are times when we need action and adventure — which the sea can also give in abundance.

The sea calms the most restless spirit, perhaps because of its own perpetual but never-repeating movement. Men who will relax nowhere else will sit for hours on a beach, or upon the deck of a ship, watching the waves weave their endless patterns. The cares and turmoils of everyday life seem unimportant when we contemplate the sea.

Like all other things, the sea will not endure forever. But by our standards it is eternal. As we look across its moving surface, remembering that it has scarcely changed since the first man saw the light of day, our minds are washed clean of the petty ambitions and jealousies and meannesses that form so large a part of everyday existence. From the waters which first gave us life we may draw not only food for our bodies and raw materials for our factories, but also refreshment for our spirit.

The sea is our greatest heritage. We are only now beginning to realize its value. Let us use it more wisely than we have used the land.

Index

Arthur C. Clarke was born in Somerset, England. He studied at King's College and the University of London where he took a B.S. degree with First Class Honors in physics and pure and applied mathematics.

During World War II he was a radar specialist with the R.A.F. and held the rank of Flight Lieutenant. Following the war he became a science editor and a TV and radio writer. Since 1951 he has devoted full time to writing, and is the author of twenty-five books as well as more than one hundred articles and short stories.

Mr. Clarke is a Fellow of the Royal Astronomical Society and has twice been chairman of the British Interplanetary Society. As a member of the Underwater Explorers Club, he has taken part in underwater exploration and photography along the Great Barrier Reef in Australia. He now makes his home in Ceylon.